CLIMB: Face Your Past, Own Your Future

Teen and Young Adult Workbook by Roderick Cunningham

Copyright © 2018 by Chief Empowerment Network, LLC

150 Commonwealth Court North
St. Petersburg, FL 33716

Published 2018 by Chief Empowerment Network, LLC.

Unless otherwise noted, all Scripture quotations are taken from the **New King James Version** of the Bible. New King James Version (NKJV) - Copyright information © 1982 by Thomas Nelson, Inc. All rights reserved. Used by permission. Scripture notations marked MSG is from The Message Bible, and KJV is from the King James Version. "Scripture taken from The Message. Copyright © 1993, 1994, 1995, 1996, 2000, 2001, 2002. Used by permission of NavPress Publishing Group."

WORKBOOK USER LICENSE AGREEMENT

Chief Empowerment Network, LLC makes no warranty, representation, or promises not expressly outlined in this Material. Chief Empowerment Network, LLC is not liable for any special, incidental, consequential, indirect or punitive damages, lost profits, or revenue because of the use of the Materials. This agreement constitutes the entire understanding between the parties and may be amended only in writing signed by both parties. This shall automatically be terminated if you breach this Agreement. Upon termination of this for any reason, you shall return the Materials to Chief Empowerment Network, LLC without refund. This agreement is governed by the laws of the State of Florida and the United States of America.

The Materials are protected by U.S. and international copyright and trademark laws. Unauthorized use of the Materials will constitute breach of the copyright and trademark infringement, which will result in serious legal action. If you have any questions concerning proper legal use of the Materials, please contact Chief Empowerment Network, LLC at 813-380-8045 or www.chiefempowerment.com.

For customized training materials and/or to become a certified trainer of this material, contact Chief Empowerment Network, LLC directly at 813-380-8045.

Youth Social/Emotional Training:
To book Mr. Cunningham directly for a keynote address, seminar, coaching or to train mentors, teachers, parents, law enforcement, or young people in your community about social/emotional wellness, please contact his team at info@rodcunninghamspeaks.com

No part of this publication may be resold (in part or whole), file shared, copied, reproduced, modified, stored in a retrieval system, transmitted, or made public in any form, without the express written permission of Chief Empowerment Network, LLC.

This workbook is not intended for resale (without prior permission).

TERMS OF USE: This workbook is for individuals, parents, teachers, mentors, etc. It is also designed for large year-long and summer youth programs, church youth programs, juvenile diversion programs, etc. In a group/workshop setting (6 or more participants), training must be conducted by facilitators who have been approved and/or certified by *Chief Empowerment Network, LLC*. The workbook and the other materials for this workshop are to be used only under the terms and conditions of the agreement between Chief Empowerment Network, LLC and the entity arranged with Chief Empowerment Network, LLC.

Layout assisted by www.diverseskillcenter.com

Book Cover Layout: VI Covers and Above Brand (www.abovebrand.com) Marketing

Book Cover Photos: Male: Deposit Photos (Credit: UTBP)

Female: iStock Photos (Credit: Filadendron)

Back Cover Photo: Kirkland Small, Above Brand Photography (www.abovebrand.com)

Inside photography: Noah Diggs, Gibbs HS, St. Petersburg, FL

Inside Graphics: Meredith Rucker of Meredith Creative Marketing, Inc.

Special Thanks: Terri Lipsey Scott of Carter G. Woodson African-American History

   Museum in St. Petersburg, FL

Inside illustrations: Erika D. Wyckoff, Tampa, FL

Conceptual Assistant: Dexter Wyckoff, II, Tampa, FL

Edited by: Valerie Cunningham, Erik Smith, D. Simon and

   Eli Gonzalez /Lil Barcaski of The Ghost Publishing

Printed in the United States of America

ISBN-13: 9-781732-265905

ISBN-10: 1732-265909

TABLE OF CONTENTS

"The man who does not read good books has no advantage over the man who cannot read them."

— Mark Twain

"You own your feelings. You own your thoughts. You control both. No one has the right to any of it—to any of you without your permission."

— Carlos Wallace

INTRODUCTION

CLIMB is a set of strategies designed to help you climb out of emotional isolation. This workbook serves as a coaching tool to help you face unresolved issues or past hurts that often keep you from living your best life. Whether the past hurt stems from parental abandonment, loss of a loved one, abuse, or bullying, you cannot overcome what you refuse to confront. When you haven't been given the tools to properly confront the pain of the past, it often leads to deviant behavior such as gang activity, gambling, alcoholism, drug abuse, crime and sexual promiscuity. Unresolved pain can also manifest itself in non-violent ways such as eating disorders, being consistently withdrawn, excessive gaming, and listening to explicit music, all of which can negatively impact your future.

In this workbook, I discuss how life's negative events can put us all in an emotional hole. Instead of judging you for bad decisions you may make or for shutting people out of your life while in the emotional hole, I get in the hole with you because I recognize the hole. I was in that same hole throughout my teenage years, then returned to a much deeper version of that hole in my mid-forties. It wasn't until I faced my past that I was able to own my future. So, grab the ladder tight as I reveal the five specific steps to CLIMB out of your emotional hole.

This workbook can be used as a standalone guide for teenagers and young adults to live an empowered lifestyle. It was designed to be taught by a teacher, mentor, or parent on a face-to-face basis. Additionally, it is also designed for large year-long and summer youth programs, church youth programs, juvenile diversion programs, etc. You will find this book to be very useful in understanding human behavior. I purposefully did not list any medical and/or clinical terminology in this book because, in my experience, it tends to get lost in translation with the average young person. I talk about behavior that many of us see on a daily basis but don't understand. I am humbled by the fact that I've individually counseled, mentored, and empowered over 9,000 teenagers and young adults between the ages of 10 and 30 over the last six years who entrusted their innermost secrets with me. There were specific patterns that emerged from these sessions that I am able to bring to the masses to help us understand why we do what we do. I continue to stay in the trenches as a youth empowerment coach who provides social and emotional wellness services to 40-50 young men and women each week, helping young people live their best lives.

Teachers/Counselors/School Psychologists:

This book will help you understand what is going on with the young person that you are responsible for during school hours. It helps to understand certain things that may be seen or heard by a student that may trigger an explosive reaction in an otherwise calm classroom. Too many times we intervene "after" a child has an emotional outburst of anger or frustration instead of peeling back the onion to find the source. Additionally, instead of suspending a student from school for three days for bad behavior, your school district should consider teaching this workbook on Saturday morning for 4 hours (once per week). All students who would have otherwise been suspended during the week, will now attend Saturday school instead. As you know, when kids are suspended, they are normally at home alone getting into more trouble and they fall behind in class, leading to further frustration. This course can also be taught while a student is participating in the In-School Suspension Program. Many of our inner-city youth lead their lives and many situations with negative emotions. Leading with negative emotions have gotten the young and old suspended from school, fired from work, arrested, hurt, divorced, and unfortunately, killed (during a traffic stop, an argument, road rage, etc.). Getting our emotions under control is a major step toward a highly successful life.

Community Mentors:

There are thousands of men and women who want to become mentors for our youth but don't know exactly how they can make a difference in the life of a teenager. This book will open the eyes of mentors and potential mentors around the world. If mentoring is something that interest you this book will help you to connect with young people and hopefully give you some nuggets to connect with your own children, nieces, nephews, friends, and extended family members. Every happy, successful, and goal orientated teenager is a win for all communities. The simple answer is to tell a teenager that you love them and that you are proud of them, remembering to ALWAYS keep your word.

"A person with good intentions makes promises, a person with good character keeps them."

- Eric Thomas

Parents:

There is so much that you will be able to glean from this book as it relates to understanding what is really bothering your child. I wish I had this book when I was a teenager as well as when I raised three teenagers. The great thing about children is that they are resilient. It is never too late to hit the restart button when it comes to your children. Your children adore you and are looking for a reason to give you unconditional love. They just want you to love them and tell them that you are proud of them, no matter their age. It is very possible that if you don't communicate with your teenage or adult children weekly, that they are holding something against you. This book should reveal to you what their struggles may be. Here's the million-dollar question that will help you uncover anything that your child may be holding on to:

Parental Question: Son/daughter, have I ever said or done anything to you that you have not been able to get over? Wait for it... wait for it... wait for it...

Child's Answer: Yes Mom/Dad, last year when we were... You said to me... And it hurt my feelings. I want you to believe in me and be proud of me.

Parental Answer: "I am so sorry, please forgive me, I love you unconditionally." Say these three things only, do not deviate.
You can also add this to your conversation at any time you feel comfortable, *"I am so proud of you and I am proud to be your Father/Mother".*

The phrase above works perfectly and can be done over the phone. You have to be ready for what your child tells you and don't interrupt, create excuses, downplay their feelings, get angry, get sad, or get defensive. The most common *inappropriate* parental answer is:

- "When you become an adult, you will make mistakes or decisions that you are not proud of."
- "Are you still talking about that, you need to let that go."
- "I had no idea you were holding on to this, why didn't you tell me before now?"
- "If you remember, I had just buried _____ and I was grieving."
- "Stop blaming me for your problems."

- "I was angry when I did that."
- "I'm not perfect."
- "But you don't understand."

- "I only wanted the best for you."
- "I did what I had to do at the time."
- "Grow up; life is not always kind or fair."

Avoid these statements at all costs because your apology will not appear genuine. Also, you may have used a different version of the phrases above. You may have said,

"Honey, 'IF' I have ever done anything to you, I'm sorry."

That is NOT the same thing. The original "parental question" asks them a thought provoking question and encourages them to think, speak, and for you to listen patiently. They are looking for an apology for something you did specifically. The fact that your parents or grandparents never apologized to you is not a good enough reason not to apologize to your children. Additionally, some parents may feel as though to apologize to your child is somehow making them weak, making them feel as though the world will apologize to them for being cruel. Your apology will actually make them stronger so that they have the strength to face what the world will throw at them. After the apology, you can use the materials in this book to build up your child's resiliency.

Teenagers/College Students/Young Adults:

This is a guide that you can use for the rest of your life. As a teenager, I did not have a father to guide my decision making and my mother only knew what was taught to her, so I would have loved a reference guide to show me what to do when life got confusing. This is that guide! It is packed with information that you can not only use for yourself, but it will help you identify what to do and say to help your friends, family, and co-workers in crisis. The information in this book will save you money if you had to try to figure it out on your own. It can help you make better decisions that will keep you out of trouble; it can help you focus and stay in school, and it can help you avoid having a child too young (priceless);

This book should be read cover to cover more than once. It is designed as a guide you may want to reference daily, weekly, or monthly. If you follow the guidance and do what the book suggests, your life will NEVER be the same; I guarantee it.

Chapter 1

MY PERSONAL CLIMB

"The best years of your life are the ones in which you decide your problems are your own. You do not blame them on your mother, the ecology, or the president. You realize that you control your own destiny."

– Albert Ellis

At forty-six-years-old I was at the top of my military career after spending twenty-eight years serving my country. I was responsible for over 5,000 people, mostly between the ages of 18-25. My wife had multiple businesses and we were living a great life. Suddenly, my mother passed away from complications of influenza (the flu). My life stopped as I knew it. I didn't want to go to work, I was snappy and irritated most of the time. I had to fight the spirit of depression daily. I woke up between 2:30 and 3:00 am at least four times per week. I started playing three to four-hours-per-day of mobile gaming to escape my life, and I was upset with my extended family because none of them called to check on me after the first two-weeks of burying my mother, but they did call when they wanted the stuff she left behind (car, furniture, jewelry, purses, etc.). I was an only child, my mother had me at the age of fifteen, and we had a very close and loving relationship. Although I traveled the world with the military, it never stopped my mom and I from talking at least 3-times per week.

There was nothing more humbling than to have 9,000+ individuals open up to me and share their deepest emotional hurts. After consistently recommending higher levels of professional counseling, I found that they were performing better. I knew what I needed to do to get better, but I just didn't feel like doing those things at the time. I felt that I would somehow dishonor my mother's legacy if I stopped thinking about the pain of her dying, instead of the enjoying and celebrating the memories of her life.

Setting up an Air Force mental health appointment was actually quite easy, although I procrastinated a few months before I went into action. While in the waiting room the receptionist gave me a survey to see how I was feeling that day. Did you sleep well last night? Are you feeling tired and hopeless? Do you feel worthless? Do you feel as though you want to hurt yourself or others?

The psychologist greeted me in the lobby, walked me to his office and said, "Chief, what would you like to talk about"? I said, "Doc, my mom died two months ago. I wake up at 3:00 am at least four nights per week. I'm irritable and snappy toward my wife, my mother-in-law lives with me and has Stage 4 Lung Cancer and currently is in the intensive care unit at the base hospital, and my wife is worried and concerned about me and her mother. So, what should I do?" I also explained that the noise of the hospital equipment made me nervous when the alarms would sound because it reminded me of when my mom died in the intensive care unit.

As you can see, I was unbalanced with a broken heart, and was currently in a deep emotional hole. My life had been turned upside down in a very short period of time. It was unreal for me. The great thing for me was that I knew I was in an emotional hole. I knew how to get out, although I didn't feel like doing what was necessary to CLIMB out.

Five months after my mom died, my mother-in-law passed away. This sent me deeper in a hole as I was very close to my mother-in-law and experiencing my wife's pain sent me down deeper. During this period my psychologist asked if I wanted to see a psychiatrist who could prescribe me anti-depressant medication. Although I was in an emotional hole and knew what I needed to do to climb out, I was curious to see what the psychiatrist would say. As I sat with the psychiatrist, he seemed a lot more formal than my psychologist. He listened to me talk, then asked if I wanted him to prescribe me an anti-depressant. I refused the medicine and continued my counseling sessions with the psychologist. Here are some of the things I began to do immediately:

1. I prayed, and my wife encouraged me to read specific verses in the Bible.

2. I listened to four different spiritual/motivational messages per day by Pastor Joel Osteen and Bishop T.D. Jakes on satellite radio and YouTube.

3. I found purpose by helping young people (aged 14-35) climb out of their emotional hole by mentoring enlisted personnel, officers, and teens at juvenile detention centers around Mississippi where I was stationed.

4. I forgave everyone in my life who hurt me or disappointed me

Although my psychologist was very helpful to me because I needed to vent and be very transparent, I felt as though he didn't give me the "detailed" advice or guidance that I needed. The sessions were limited to one hour and I was only allowed about six sessions before an evaluation occurred to see if the psychologist would continue to see me.

I personally feel as though the mental health industry should add life coaching as a follow-up to psychologists. The life coach focuses on your future and spending time with you to help you focus and re-insert yourself into society and your workplace. They give advice and coaching on living your best life. Primary Care Physicians should be able to write a prescription for coaching.

But until that happens, if you simply follow the steps laid out for you in this book, you will find yourself feeling much better about your past and you will own your future. Some have been able to decrease their antidepressant medication (consult your physician first). Additionally, Neurolinguistics Programming and Time Line Therapy® (Dr. Tad James) really helped me take full control of my thoughts and my reactions to things in my life that may have made me angry or sad in the past.

According to the Centers for Disease Control (CDC), 1 in 8 Americans aged 12 years and over, take antidepressant medication, and the United States of America is ranked #1 in the world for prescribing these types of drugs. [01]
Unfortunately, some people don't believe that they can actually CLIMB out of the emotional hole and live a better, more balanced life, but it can happen for anyone who is willing to make the change.

We take in information through our five senses: Touch, smell, taste, hearing, and sight. Our mind then processes this information based on our values, beliefs, decisions, and memories. We then filter the information to determine how our minds will decide what to do with it, which gives us our "personal" internal representation (what it means to us) and that is developed through sound, feeling, pictures, smells, tastes, etc.

For example, if I wake up because I *smell* smoke, my mind processes the information based on my memory that wherever there is smoke, there is fire. My personal internal representation displays a picture in my head of a fire, so I jump out of bed to investigate. If I had never smelled smoke before, then I would not respond the same way and simply go back to sleep. I may even argue with my spouse by saying, "I didn't get out of bed because I didn't think anything was wrong, because I have never smelled smoke before." Also, I might say, "Where I am from, people use burn pits all the time to stay warm, so I figured it was the neighbors burn pit."

Using the smoke example above, one person may jump out of bed to investigate and the other may stay in bed because they don't think it is anything serious. In actuality, there was a fire burning in the walls of the kitchen due to an electrical issue with the house. One husband acted on it, the other one didn't, but there was still a fire.

With that said, one person may realize that their past trauma is causing them to act out and make bad decisions, so they take action to CLIMB and begin to live a better life. Just because another person says, "I'm fine", it doesn't mean his bad decision making is not related to his father's incarceration. One man acted, the other ignored it, "but the house was still on fire".

Don't Call People Crazy

Most don't realize they are living in an emotional hole and talking about these issues are not a part of our everyday lives. As we speak about the negative emotions and behavior of others, we sometimes give them undesirable labels like crazy or psycho, and no one wants that type of label. We all need an emotional adjustment from time to time to help us bring clarity to our thoughts and emotions. Similarly, our backs may get out of alignment and we need a back adjustment. Never refer to anyone as crazy. Get in the hole with them and help them CLIMB. Show empathy to others as we don't know what they go through just to get out of bed each day.

After reviewing Tables 1-1, 1-2. 1-3, and 1-4, you may realize that you are in an emotional hole. Some holes will be deeper than others. This book is designed to help you out of the hole. Some people may not like the terms I use (unbalanced, broken hearted, or emotional hole), but instead of focusing on the terms, focus on getting an adjustment so that you can live a better life. Human beings are not designed to handle heartbreak after heartbreak. Let's CLIMB together.

SPIRITUAL REFERENCES:

Anything is Possible
"I can do all things through Christ who strengthens me."
- **Philippians 4:13 (NKJV)**

FAMOUS QUOTES:

"Do not let the memories of your past limit the potential of your future. There are no limits to what you can achieve on your journey through life, except in your mind."
- **Roy T. Bennett**

TAKEAWAYS:

1. If you don't take action, your life will remain the same.

2. When you find yourself in a difficult situation, simply ask "If I didn't believe it was impossible, what could I do about it?

AFFIRMATIONS: (Recite each morning)

I will take at least one step toward achieving my goal today.

TIME TO CLIMB:

Exercise 1: DAILY MOTIVATION

Materials needed: Smart Phone / YouTube App

It is important for our brains to hear positive, uplifting messages each day. A dose of motivation each day can help you achieve your daily goals and it creates a positive mindset.

1. Choose a motivational speaker below and go to YouTube and search for their names

   - Les Brown (Speaker)
   - Eric Thomas (Speaker)
   - Tony Robins (Life Coach)
   - TD Jakes (Spiritual Leader)
   - Joel Osteen (Spiritual Leader)

2. Listen to at least a 20-minute motivational message each day. Listening to the same message over multiple days can be effective as well.

Chapter 2

FACE YOUR PAST

"No matter what a man's past may have been, his future is spotless."

– John R. Rice

When you are eight-years-old, and your parents get a divorce, you fall into an emotional hole, and you don't know it. When you are twelve-years-old, and you visit your angry father, who hits you for lying to him, although you didn't lie, you fall deeper into that same emotional hole because you don't "feel" unconditional love from your biological father and you don't feel as though he is proud of you. When you are sixteen-years-old your grandmother passes away. Because you felt that your grandmother was the only person that that truly understood you, loved you unconditionally, and consistently told you that she was proud of you, you find yourself even deeper in that hole. When your best friend is killed in a car accident during your freshman year in college, you fall even deeper in that same emotional hole. Then, when you are twenty-eight-years-old, you get a divorce from the person that you thought you'd be with for the rest of your life, and that person tries to take your children away from you Now, you fall even deeper in that hole.

At this point, most of your family and friends will simply look down in your hole and make comments like,

"Why are you still talking about that?"

"You need to let that go"

"What is wrong with you?"

"Get over it!"

"Your father hit you fifteen-years-ago, move on."

"Take that outside and bury it for once and for all"

"Are you crazy?"

"Just pray about it"

Unfortunately, no one teaches you "HOW" to "CLIMB" out of the hole.

To move forward with our lives effectively, we must take a hard look at where we've come from. Our childhood shapes our adulthood, whether we realize it or not.

Here are the Top 4 things that are bothering most teenagers:

1. You don't have the relationship with one of your biological parents that you DESIRE to have. **(ABANDONMENT)**

2. Someone who you truly loved has passed away (i.e., sibling, parent, grandparent, uncle, aunt, significant other, cousin, best friend, etc.) **(LOSS)**

3. You were touched inappropriately by someone older than you. **(ABUSE)**

4. Rejected by your peers. **(REJECTION)**

The presence of LOVE and acceptance makes a large difference in our emotions, which normally drives our decision-making process. Here are examples of positive and negative emotions:

1. Positive Emotions: Happy, joy, gratitude, serenity, hope, pride, inspiration, kindness, amusement, cheerfulness, and LOVE

2. Negative Emotions: Sadness, anger, anxiety, and despair

ABANDONMENT

As children, we want to receive love and acceptance from the two people who are responsible for our birth. When that love, and acceptance is present with our biological (real) parents, our emotions are in good balance and our minds are clear to make good decisions for our lives. When life gets confusing or stressful, we can receive good counsel from our parents to make even better decisions. When one or both of our biological parents are not present, does not show love and acceptance or are not good decision makers based on their own emotions, our decision-making process gets clouded and it forces us to seek comfort due to the absence of love and acceptance. We seek love, acceptance, and comfort in many different ways. We normally choose behavior that is acceptable to our parents, our friends, our family members, and/or within our community. If your mom drank alcohol as a form of comfort when she is stressed, most likely you may also "choose" to drink alcohol as a stress reliever. If your friends smoke marijuana for comfort, you may also "choose" marijuana for comfort. If your father gets angry when he is stressed, you may also "choose" anger. In Chapter 2, we will discuss other negative and positive areas where many people seek comfort.

LOSS

Unfortunately, death is a part of life. We all know that someday our loved ones will pass away. No matter their age, they will pass away too soon for our emotions to handle it. When we are grieving the death of a loved one, we will again seek comfort from somewhere (sex/drugs/alcohol/cigarettes), someone (gang/boyfriend/girlfriend), or we will choose destructive behavior (fighting/stealing/selling drugs). Also, some teenage boys may seek comfort by asking their girlfriend to start a family by having a baby.

> *Chuck was 21 when his 22-year-old brother was killed in a car accident. Chuck took his brother's death very hard. He started hanging out late at night with local drug dealers. His mother begged him to get counseling and to stop hanging out so late. Chuck was so hurt, that he really didn't care what happened to him and he didn't listen to the wise counsel of his mother and father. Chuck has been in prison now for five years. He has three boys ages six, seven, and eight-years-old who are growing up without their father. His six-year-old son is very disruptive in school and has threatened suicide multiple times. Chuck regrets not listening to his parents and not being there for his boys. He now has plenty of time to think about his actions while he is in jail.*

Counseling and coaching are great ways to deal with the death of a loved one. We will continue to discuss counseling in future chapters.

ABUSE

Inappropriate touching is more common than we all know. Six years ago, I knew only three people who were touched inappropriately by a family member, a step-parent, an uncle/aunt, another kid in the neighborhood, etc. Today, I know 161 people who have experienced this horrific act. If this has happened to you, no matter how insignificant you think it may have been, it is time to get counseling from a professional counselor. The counselor will help you sort through the feelings of isolation, abandonment, sadness, anxiety, anger, weakness, etc. After many sessions (6-10) with the counselor, it is best to follow-up with a life coach who will help you craft an awesome future for your life and your family. If you don't receive counseling immediately, this childhood traumatic event "will" affect you for the rest of your life. Counseling and life coaching will help you to remove the negative emotions associated with the memory of this event.

REJECTION

Bullying, including cyber bullying using social media, is a major problem with youth today. It is important for fourteen-year-olds to be accepted and respected by their peers. Seventy-five percent of all kids report they have experienced being bullied. I have found that the best way to deal with bullies is to do the following:

1. Report them to a teacher or counselor.
2. Ignore them.

If you choose, you can remain anonymous when reporting them to faculty. The bully is most likely bullying multiple people, so they will have a hard time figuring it out.

We call Cyber-bullies "haters". A hater's job is to hate others who are doing good things.

> *Julie is a hater and she talks about everyone on social media. Each day she hates on a new person. She is good at her job, although she forgets that she hated on you last week, because she has hated on ten other people since then.*

When you understand your worth and your personal power as a human being, you will ignore people who talk about you, because they don't matter. Just make sure that when you become a high school senior that you don't start bullying underclassmen.

Losing friendships and romantic relationships can be very tough. Many times, we may find comfort in these relationships because of issues with parents, death of a loved one, or inappropriate touching when you were younger. On the other hand, some kids are naturally kind and caring people and they really value true friendships and they are really bummed out when a relationship ends. Many times, relationships end because of a misunderstanding. It is best to go to the person and talk about what happened. I met my best friend at a school dance at twelve-years-old and we had many disagreements and stopped being friends about five times before graduating high school. We are still friends today, thirty-eight years later. The easy answer here is to just say "I'm sorry," even if you don't feel you did anything wrong. I'm sure being right is not more important than your friendship. Apologize and move on with life.

WHAT IS LOVE?

Everyone wants to be loved. If you ask ten people to define love you will get ten different answers. We all want love, but very few know how to give love.

Love is patient, love is kind. It does not envy, it does not boast, it is not proud. It does not dishonor others, it is not self-seeking, it is not easily angered, it keeps no record of wrongs.

Love does not delight in evil but rejoices with the truth. It always protects, always trusts, always hopes, always perseveres. [02]

Love is a daily "action" we take to show someone how much we care about them. There are seven different types of love according to the ancient Greeks:[03]

Storge Love: Love for your child. This is the natural, effortless love that parents have for their children. This is the love that is keenly aware of sacrifice, acceptance, and forgiveness.

Philia Love: Brotherly Love. Considered platonic and is the love you have for your brother or a great friend.

Agape Love: Love for humanity. This love is selfless, empathetic, and compassionate and is given without expecting anything in return. It is the closest to unconditional love.

Eros Love: Romantic love. Defined as divine lust or beauty.

Ludus Love: Playful love when one is flirtatious and likes to tease and laugh.

Pragma: Everlasting love between a married couple which develops over a long period of time and requires a profound understanding between lovers.

Philautia: *Love for yourself.* It is divided into two kinds: One that is pure selfish and seeks wealth, fame, and pleasure and the other is healthy love that we give ourselves.

What is unconditional love? It is an affection that does not have conditions or limitations. Many consider it complete love as it has no bounds and is unchanging. It is a term used between couples in highly committed relationships, between close friends, and between family members.

Most importantly is that it <u>separates</u> the individual from his or her behaviors.

Here's a simple example of love without conditions:

> *You acquire a new family member, a poodle. The poodle steals the heart of the entire family immediately because she is cuddly, cute, active, and loves to play. Then one day she pees on the carpet. Do you stop loving the poodle? Probably not, but you will begin to discipline the poodle through education and training. You may even hire a dog trainer, but you don't stop loving the poodle.*

What is conditional love? Love that is earned. "If you do this for me, then I will love you."

Love should never have to be earned. Love is a grace that we give each other. We should love everyone in the world, unconditionally. Realizing that we all are doing the best that we can do, based on how we were raised, living in a hectic world.

Unconditional love is a long-term **_choice_** and promise that we make **_daily_** to commit a heartfelt, kind, and **_caring action toward a person that is imperfect_**.

Do we all agree that everyone wants to be loved unconditionally? We want to be loved just as we are, and we don't want people to feel as though they need to change us in order for them to accept us or spend time with us.

As a fourteen-year-old we want to know that our biological parents are there for us to help us navigate our lives. We feel as though they would understand us best because we are descendants of theirs. When mom or dad is tired, irritated or too busy to engage us, then we want the capability of going to the other parent for love, comfort, and understanding. This is in no way to discount the role of a step-parent or adoptive parent. It is simply to help you understand what our natural needs are as human beings.

Once a fourteen-year-old has the stability of love and comfort from parents, then they are free to develop healthy relationships with friends and classmates. They may not engage parents often at this age, but to know that parents are available, supportive, stress how proud they are, and attend school and sporting events, are important aspects of the child-parent relationship.

JIMMY

Jimmy and his mother recently moved from Indiana to Florida. "Wow, this school is enormous," said Jimmy as he was searching for his freshman homeroom class. As he watched the seniors run around campus on the first day of school laughing and joking around, he was astonished at how big, how confident, and mature they were. "How will I ever fit in at this school," Jimmy thought to himself.

One month after starting high school, Jimmy still hadn't made any real friends. He had a pretty big crush on Felecia, but he never even said hello to her. He wondered if she even knew he existed.

Jimmy had always been a very intelligent kid with a well-crafted vocabulary and a very proper dialect. "Bro, why do you talk like that," said Chris. "Like what," said Jimmy. "You talk so proper. We don't talk like that around here. Where are you from?" said Chris. "I'm from Indiana and I didn't realize my dialect was any different than anyone else's. I speak how I speak." said Jimmy. "Whatever Bro," said Chris, laughing as he walked away with his arms around his girlfriend Amelia.

That exchange with Chris really bothered Jimmy. He began looking in the mirror each day to practice a more southern dialect when at school or around his classmates. He also changed his "preppy" style of clothing and his hairstyle.

The pressure for Jimmy to fit-in caused him to create an entirely different persona so that he would be accepted at school. Each day upon arriving home after school, Jimmy dropped that false persona because he did not want to have to maintain the persona in his own home. He wanted to be able to relax and be himself. Jimmy felt as though he didn't have to put on airs at home and that his mom and dad would love him unconditionally. He thought to himself, "Mom and dad, if I am stupid, then so are you, because you made me, right?"

Many times, Jimmy's mom, Melissa, had a long day at work and when she arrived at home in the evening, she was tired. She too was putting on airs at work so that she could fit in to the company's culture. When she arrived at home, she too wanted to relax and be herself. "Did you pick your sister up from school? Did you do your homework? Did you wash the dishes? Did you wash the clothes? Did you make us some dinner?" asked Melissa with an exhausted tone. Standing in front of his mother looking like a dear staring at headlights, he was startled when his mother said, "Boy, do you hear me talking to you? Did you get all of your chores done?"

"No ma'am," he said. "Are you kidding me? You didn't do anything? Please go to your room. I don't want to look at you at this moment," said Melissa.

As Jimmy walked to his room, he didn't feel that his mother's love was unconditional. He thought to himself, "If I don't do these things, then she won't love me."

Jimmy began questioning his life.

"Does mom know that I had a hard day at school today?"
"Does anyone care that the girl I love doesn't know I even exist?"
"Does anyone care that I don't have any friends?"
"Does anyone love me?"
"Does anyone care about me?"
"Does anyone understand who I am and the things that I want to do?"
"Does my mom care?"
"My dad will understand me, I will just go and talk to him."

As Jimmy took one step towards the bedroom, he realized that his biological father no longer lived in the house because his parents divorced last year, and his Dad lived in Indiana with a new family. There is now a disheartened feeling that came over Jimmy. Jimmy consciously or unconsciously realized that there was a major void in his life.

Jimmy didn't feel unconditional love from either of the two people who were responsible for his life at this vital point of life as a young teenager. This was where Jimmy started to develop a deeper emotional hole in his life. Jimmy experienced his first hole when his father and mother divorced when he was twelve-years-old. His hole got deeper because he and his father only talk on birthdays and holidays although Jimmy wanted a stronger relationship with his father. Jimmy wanted to talk to his father at least five days per week, although he never expressed that to his mother or father.

Jimmy didn't feel as though he had anyone to talk to and express his feelings to. It was important for Jimmy to communicate effectively with his mother and father to let them know how he felt, how much he still needed their love and acceptance, and how often he wanted to talk. If Jimmy refused to communicate and take his pain into adulthood, these feelings could follow him well into his fifties and sixties.

Since we were discussing LOVE earlier in this chapter, what body part comes to mind when we think about LOVE? Many would say the heart. With that said, if you are in an emotional hole, then I would venture to say that you have a BROKEN HEART.

BROKEN HEART = EMOTIONAL HOLE

As a parent who raised three adult children myself, I can tell you that all parents love their children unconditionally. But based on the parents' own childhood experiences, including their relationship with their own biological mother or father, they may have a hard time showing unconditional love. Parents want the best for their children. Fourteen-years-old can be a tough age for both the child and the parent, especially if the parent has multiple children who they may be raising in a single-parent household.

QUESTIONS:

1. Do you love yourself?   THERE'S NOBODY BETTER | A LOT | A LITTLE | NO

2. Do you think positive thoughts about yourself?   YES | NO | SOMETIMES

3. Do you believe that you can achieve the desires of your heart?
   YES | NO | SOMETIMES

4. Is it important to you to show love to others (kindness, patience, empathy, respect)?   YES | NO | SOMETIMES | I DON'T CARE ABOUT OTHERS

5. Is it important to you to receive love from others (kindness, patience, empathy, respect)? YES | NO | SOMETIMES | I DON'T CARE HOW OTHERS TREAT ME

6. What is the difference between unconditional love and conditional love?

   _____

   _____

7. Who do you feel loves you unconditionally?

   _____

   _____

8. Is it important to receive unconditional love from your parents?
   YES | NO | MAYBE

9. Do you feel unconditional love from your biological (real) father?
   YES | NO | SOMETIMES | I DON'T KNOW | HE IS DECEASED | WE'VE NEVER MET

10. Do you feel unconditional love from your biological (real) mother?
    YES | NO | SOMETIMES | I DON'T KNOW | SHE IS DECEASED | WE'VE NEVER MET

11. Who do you love unconditionally?

    _____

    _____

SPIRITUAL REFERENCES:

1. *"Love is patient, love is kind. It does not envy, it does not boast, it is not proud. It does not dishonor others, it is not self-seeking, it is not easily angered, it keeps no record of wrongs. Love does not delight in evil but rejoices with the truth. It always protects, always trusts, always hopes, always perseveres."*
   - 1 Corinthians 13:4-7 (NIV)

2. *"Isn't this your father who created you, who made you and gave you a place on Earth? Read up on what happened before you were born; dig into the past, understand your roots. Ask your parents what it was like before you were born; ask the old-ones, they'll tell you a thing or two."*
   - Deuteronomy 32:6 (MSG)

FAMOUS QUOTES:

1. *"The greatest happiness of life is the conviction that we are loved; loved for ourselves, or rather, loved in spite of ourselves."*
   - Victor Hugo

2. *"I saw that you were perfect, and so I loved you. Then I saw that you were not perfect, and I loved you even more."*
   - Angelita Lim

TAKEAWAYS:

1. Everyone deserves to be loved unconditionally because we are simply imperfect humans.

2. Top 4 things bothering most teenagers:
   a. Not having the relationship you desire with a biological parent
   b. Death of a friend or loved one
   c. Inappropriate touching
   d. Bullying or rejection from a friend or significant other

3. We all want to know two things from our biological parents:
   a. Do you love me unconditionally?
   b. Are you proud of me?

4. The love of step-parents and adoptive parents are different. This parent/child relationship is more of an appreciation of your love.
   a. Thank you for loving me, my siblings, and my mom/dad.
   b. Thank you for providing my basic needs of food, clothing, and shelter.
   c. Thank you for teaching me how to be a man/woman or how a man/woman is supposed to treat me.
   d. Thank you for raising me in a loving household.
   e. Thank you for teaching me how to play sports.
   f. Thank you for being present at my school and after school events.
   g. Thank you for providing a disciplined household filled with love.
   h. Thank you for your solid counsel and mentoring over the years.

AFFIRMATIONS: (Recite each morning)

1. I will tell my parents that I love them unconditionally every day.
2. I will LOVE everyone unconditionally.
3. I will communicate often with my parents and inform them of my need to be loved and supported.

TIME TO CLIMB:

Exercise 1: IDENTIFY WHAT IS BOTHERING YOU

Materials needed: None

1. Strained or non-existent relationship with a biological parent

2. Death of a friend or loved one

3. Inappropriate touching

4. Bullying or rejection of a friend or girlfriend/boyfriend

NOTE: If you feel that you have experienced #3 above, please call
1-855-4-VICTIM (1-855-484-2846) to speak to a professional who will instruct you on what to do next. You may also reach out to a school counselor or principal.

Exercise 2: OPEN THE LINES OF COMMUNICATION

Materials needed: Cell phone, email, or social media account

1. If you are able to do so, send a text or go on social media and reach out to the parent with the strained relationship. Tell them that you want a stronger relationship and it's important that you both communicate several times per week.

    Sample Text/Email/Social Media: Hello Dad, I know we haven't communicated a lot lately and that makes me sad. I would like for us to talk more often, at least 4 times-a-week. It doesn't matter what we talk about, I just want to talk to you. You are my Dad and I need you in my life. Here are some facts about me: I have two best friends, Katie and John. I love to play soccer. I am an avid reader and I'm currently reading a spy novel. I am trying out for the basketball team next year. I am a pretty good piano player, and I have a 3.5 GPA. It is important for me to know that you love me and are proud of me. I love you and look forward to hearing your voice soon.

2. If you can't reach out to the parent, never met the parent, or the parent is deceased, then discuss your feelings with your custodial parent or guardian. Let them know that you love them and appreciate them for raising you. Let them know that you are struggling with your desire to have that missing parent be a part of your life.

3. If someone you love that has passed away, come up with some ideas on how you can honor the memory of that person. Here are some examples:

   a. Raise money annually to present a $500 college scholarship in their name to a student at your high school.
   b. Volunteer to help others at their favorite charity.
   c. Create a business or charitable foundation in their name.

   Think of other ways that you can honor the person who passed away.

4. If you are being bullied, then it is time to talk about it. Report the bullying to your teachers or counselors. You are not the first student to be bullied and you won't be the last. School staff has experience in this area, so trust the process.

5. If you and your friends are not speaking to each other, then it is time to communicate and calmly talk about what happened. Many times, it is simply a misunderstanding.

Exercise 3: VISION BOARDING

Materials needed: Magazines, glue sticks, pens, markers, poster board, scissors, etc. All can be found at a local dollar store.

1. If you are in a classroom, break up into groups of three.

2. Bring magazines for each group to share.

3. Encourage students to search Google Images to find images of homes, family, vacations, careers, etc. Ask them to print out the images and bring them to class.

4. This exercise can be started in class but finished at home.

"SAMPLE" VISION BOARD

DESIRE
+
BELIEF
+
ACTION
=
RESULTS!

Dream Home

Dream Kitchen

Dream Swimming Pool

$200K per year
in income by age 30

Bachelors Degree by age 22
Masters Degree by age 24
MD, J.D., or PhD by age 30

Quiet Space for Reading,
Praying and Meditating

Dream Family

Corporate CEO

Dream Wedding

Dream Vacation

Medical Nurse/Doctor

Love and Relationship

MIAMI STATE
UNIVERSITY

Dream Car

EVERYTHING IS POSSIBLE

Entrepreneur

I BELIEVE I CAN DO THIS!

I pray that I learn HOW to control my
thoughts, it *WILL* dictate my future.
I will not allow negative people to
control my thoughts.

Chapter 3

YOUR CHOICES

"We've all got both light and dark inside of us. What matters is the part we choose to act on. That's who we really are.

– J.K. Rowling

When a person is in an emotional hole, they will begin to express certain emotions and behavior where they either act out or shut others out. Please take a moment and check the boxes to determine your "choice" of behavior.

Common vices, bad emotions, or bad behavior (ACTING OUT): (Check all that apply, since age 11)

Table 3-1

	BAD BEHAVIOR		VICES		BAD EMOTIONS
	Fighting		Alcohol		Anger
	Skipping school		Gambling		Bad *attitude* toward parents
	Bullying		Marijuana		Bad *attitude* toward teachers
	Lying / exaggerating your achievements		Sexual promiscuity (sex w/more than one partner)		Emotional Outbursts (yelling/crying)
	Stealing		Pornography		Highly irritable
	Gossiping/mean spirited		Cigarettes		
	Cheating in school		Cheating on your mate		
	Hanging w/friends who makes bad choices				

Common ways to SHUT others OUT: (Check all the apply, since age 11)

Table 3-2

	DISCONNECTED BEHAVIOR		BAD EMOTIONS		OTHER BEHAVIORS
	Reading a lot		Grief		Overeating or not eating
	Pushing parents away		Cold-heartedness		Low self-esteem
	Lots of time alone in room		Sadness		Painting fingernails black and wearing a black trench coat
	Won't express how you truly feel		Easily bored		
	Distant		Jealousy		Revenge seeking
	Do not disturb on bedroom door		Fear/Doubt		Cutting yourself
	Do not disturb on forehead		Anxiety		Thoughts of death or suicide
	Putting on headphones, listening to music for hours (sometimes *explicit music)*				Disinterested in personal appearance
	Long hours of video gaming				Pulling your hair out

Note 1: Table 3-1 and 3-2 can start as early as six-years-old. I recently coached a six-year-old who had anger issues, emotional outbursts, was highly irritated, anxious, and played video games for hours at a time. This young man was adopted by a family member, his biological father was in prison, and he visited his biological mom every two weeks. His biggest heartbreak was that his mother is raising his three younger siblings, but not raising him. He said, "The anger is all in my head and my body." "What can you do to control it?" I asked. He said, "I can't. It's too strong."

I referred his parents to a family counselor who can design a program to help his biological mother, his adopted mother, and the little boy. Although the adopted mother can do more for this little boy financially and emotionally, the boy wants to be with his biological mother. If his biological mother is struggling, he wants to struggle with her, in love.

This little boy is very intelligent, but very emotional. His emotions will beat out his intelligence most of the time. Without unconditional love from his biological parents, counseling and male mentorship, it would NOT be hard to project the future of this little boy. It is nice that his adopted mother buys him things and loves on him, but he also needs to know that his real parents love him unconditionally and are proud of him. This is simply how we are designed as human beings and we can't run from that fact.

Many adults participate in the same vices listed in Tables 3-1 and 3-2 and have learned how to hide them from people outside of their family. It mostly reveals itself when the adult gets highly stressed (i.e., employment problems, problems with finances, relationship issues, death of a friend or family member, trouble with law enforcement, etc.) When we get stressed, we reach for something to COMFORT us and make us feel better. The most common COMFORT is overeating, cigarettes, fighting, alcohol, drugs, pornography, and sex. One of my goals in this book is to teach you how to eliminate stress from your life. If you eliminate stress from your life, then you won't search for these comforts that can possibly destroy your family, friendships, and even harm your chances of a job promotion.

QUESTIONS:

1. Do you find that you mostly act out or shut people out?   **ACT OUT | SHUT OUT**

2. Total up both areas from Table 3-1 and Table 3-2. How many areas did you identify? _____ (2 = Very Balanced, 3-4 = Average Teenager, 5 or above = Schedule time with an adult mentor and/or counselor)

   Note: If you scored 3 and above, this book will show you exactly what to do to balance your life and live an awesome life full of purpose, wealth, and abundance.

3. Are you carrying hurt from something that happened as a child?
   YES | NO | SOMETIMES | I DON'T KNOW

4. Do you know a friend or family member who may be carrying childhood pain?

   Friend 1: _____

   Friend 2: _____

   Family Member 1: _____

   Family Member 2: _____

5. Are you comfortable with the list of things that you checked off or would you like to change?

   I AM COMFORTABLE WITH ME | I AM OPEN TO BECOMING A BETTER ME

6. Are you interested in discovering your purpose in life and finding your dream career that lines up with your purpose?

   NO, MY LIFE IS ALREADY PLANNED OUT | YES, I AM OPEN TO THE POSSIBILITIES

7. Would you like to live a more peaceful, prosperous life, that leads to healthy relationships with your parents, your children (or future children), your significant other, your best friend, and your teachers/supervisors/business partners?

   NO, I LIKE SHUTTING PEOPLE OUT | YES, I AM READY TO LEARN AND GROW

Life's Not Fair

Life has a way of putting us all in an emotional hole at some point in our lives. Here is more evidence that you may be in an emotional hole right now:(Check all the apply)

Table 3-3

Anxiety attacks to include test taking anxiety	Disturbed sleep patterns: - Awaken between 2:30-3:00 AM and don't know why (2-3 nights per week) - Can't sleep
Prescribed anti-depressants	Constant need for attention or adoration
Constant feelings of fear or guilt	Easily hurt feelings
Consistently sad	Constant feelings of jealousy
Recent death of a friend or family member	Hard to maintain a romantic relationship longer than 6 months

1. How many days a week do you wake up between 2:30 AM and 3:00 AM?
   _____ TIMES PER WEEK | I DON'T, I'M A HARD SLEEPER

Note: Most people dismiss waking up early by saying that they wake up to urinate. Unfortunately, many times it's your heart that wakes you up. It is an indicator that something is bothering you. Have you ever heard the term, "I don't care, it's not like I'm going to lose sleep?" Well, you are losing sleep. Others may wake-up at this time because they are excited about a job, business, or an opportunity for enormous success.

2. Have you ever snuck out of the house between 2:30 AM and 3:00 AM or snuck someone into your parents' home who also couldn't sleep?
    YES | NO | MAYBE

3. Have your friends ever told you that you constantly fish for compliments or that you seek attention from others? YES | NO | SOMETIMES

4. Do you have a hard time maintaining romantic relationships past 6 months, regardless of who decided to end the relationship? YES | NO | SOMETIMES

5. Are you taking medications for attention deficit hyperactivity disorder (ADHD), depression, anxiety, bipolar disorder, post-traumatic stress disorder (PTSD), schizophrenia, etc.? YES | NO | SOMETIMES

    Note: The disorders in the question above are normally reserved for people who started out with childhood trauma, never climbing out of the emotional hole, then other traumatic life events occurred later, piling on top and pushing them down deeper in that emotional hole. That is why we must quickly climb out after the first traumatic event before more of life's traumatic events come our way. The mind of a child, although resilient, is not mature enough to handle traumatic events. Although you may see a fifty-year-old man in the flesh, you may be talking to the mind and emotions of a ten-year-old child whose father died and left him. This may become quite evident when he gets drunk or start using drugs and embarrasses himself and his family. With help, he can grow up to be that fifty-year-old healthy, wealthy, and wise man that he needs to be for his wife and children.

Chapter 4 will teach us how to climb out of the emotional hole on our journey to a life filled with joy, happiness, and abundance.

Notes:

_____

_____

_____

_____

Common Hurts

The list below are the most common childhood hurts, pains, or traumas that young people carry into their adulthood: (Check all that apply)

Table 3-4

HURT FROM BIOLOGICAL PARENTS	
Life-threatening illness of a parent	Divorce of parents
Incarceration of a parent	Death of a parent
Parent who travels too much for work/ military	Finding out that a parent had an affair, tearing the family unit apart
Parental abuse of alcohol or drugs and/or the abuse you suffered because of it	Never meeting your mother or father
Unacceptance by biological mother/father	Feeling misunderstood by parents
Perception of parents playing favorites amongst your siblings	Not accepting of child's sexual orientation
Sparingly attends sports and school activities	Don't support their child's aspirations
Parents who give their kids up for adoption or sent them to live with a family member (i.e. grandmother, aunt, etc.). It hurts even more if that parent eventually raises other children	Not interested in child's creative abilities (music, art, acting, clothing design, photography, hair, nails, makeup, daydreaming of a better future, community service, etc.)
Lack of love, hugs, affection, and not hearing "I love you and I am proud of you."	Verbal and/or physical abuse by parents toward the child or their siblings
A workaholic parent, or one with multiple jobs, who never has time to listen, talk, or help (lack of quality time)	One parent states that they "HATE" the other parent, then later states that you look and act just like that parent.
Does not allow the child to be themselves or they push too hard	Parental comparison of others' success in school, sports, or other activities
Parents not buying you the gifts that you want or think that you deserve	Watching one parent physically or emotionally abuse the other
Parents who are physically available, but emotionally absent (i.e. angry, sad, distant, or full of anxiety or grief)	Parents who make promises, but never keeps them. (i.e., I'm coming to get you, then never shows).
Not feeling physically or emotionally protected	Homelessness (living in shelters)
Parent not attending your wedding or high school graduation	Parent telling you "NO" when you ask to live with them.

Table 3-4 (Continued)

HURT FROM SIBLINGS		
Witnessing pain or injustice toward a sibling		Sibling not accepting you for who you are as a person
Death/suicide of a sibling		Terminal illness of a sibling
Extreme jealousy		

HURT FROM BEST FRIENDS		
Best friends not treating/supporting you the way that you treat/support them		Witnessing pain or injustice toward your best friend
Death/suicide of a best friend		Harsh judgement by your best friend

HURT FROM OTHERS		
Forced abortion by an adult		Bad break-up of a romantic relationship
Witnessing pain or injustice toward your mother or father		Inappropriate touching, rape, or violation by anyone, especially someone in authority (childhood trauma)
Your supervisor fired you, creating a threat to the survival of you and your family		Unfairly punished--others who did the same thing received less punishment
Unfairly targeted at work/school over something that you did not do		Someone at work/school lied on you and is out to get you (harassment)
Being bullied in school		

GUILT WE CARRY AGAINST OURSELVES		
Teenage abortion		When a friend or loved one commits suicide or dies in an accident
Death of our child		When we are responsible for hurting/killing someone else

The things that you checked off above in Table 3-4 may be the event that will allow your THOUGHTS to create an IMAGE that will trigger an EMOTIONAL response like anger, sadness, guilt, hurt, or fear. Although you may have verbally forgiven the person who hurt you, mentally the pain is still there and it may be triggered by your senses (i.e., seeing, hearing, tasting, touching, or smelling). Once triggered, an emotional reaction follows, causing you to lash out or shut down. Only certain people can trigger a reaction (loved ones, friends, classmates, someone who caused you physical or mental pain, police, teachers, co-workers, or your supervisor). Sometimes your anger or sadness can be triggered by anyone who poses a threat of physical or mental harm to you or your family.

Chapter 4 will teach us what to do to overcome this pain.

Table 3-4 is not all-inclusive and is not intended for you to "blame" anyone, but it was designed to make you keenly aware of what is bothering you and when you are consciously aware of anything, you can control your feelings about it. Once you have mastered your thinking, you can master your life.

Unconditional love is what we ALL want. At the age of thirteen and fourteen, we want that unconditional love to come from our biological parents. We want to know that the two people who are responsible for our birth, love us and are proud of us. If we don't get that love from them, we not only go into an emotional hole, but we search for love from other people or places. We search for love and acceptance from teachers, coaches, gangs, churches, pastors, fraternities/sororities, cult leaders, our children, friends (even the ones who make *bad* decisions), significant others (even the ones who make *bad* decisions), dating much older men/women, dating abusive men/women, etc. We simply follow the LOVE, many times to a fault.

I must digress for a moment and say that when you start dating someone, during the first six months, you are dating their representative and not the real person. The real person shows up after six months or after the words "I Love You" are exchanged. Suddenly, they may get mean spirited, negative, and disrespectful to others in your presence, start to hang out with friends who make bad decisions, etc. You may hold on to the relationship because you remember that the representative was a kind, thoughtful person when you met them. Unfortunately, the representative is gone, never to return again (unless they are rebirthed through mind, body, and spirit). In other words, there's a chance that you will frustrate yourself because the person you fell in love with was an actor.

> Do you know a friend or family member who may be dating someone who used to be nice, kind, considerate, and loving, and they are waiting on that actor (representative) to return?

Friend: _____Family Member: _____

Note: Having children with this person will not make the actor return and love you more. Fortunately, if the actor follows the suggestions laid out in this book and climbs out of their own emotional hole, they may actually grow up and become the person of your dreams, again.

SPIRITUAL REFERENCES:

1. *"Don't be too fond of sleep; you'll end up in the poorhouse. Wake up and get up; then there'll be food on the table."*
   - **Proverbs 20:13 (MSG)**

2. *"Evil people are restless unless they're making trouble; They can't get a good night's sleep unless they've made life miserable for somebody. Perversity is their food and drink, violence their drug of choice."*
   - **Proverbs 4:16 (MSG)**

3. *"Therefore, humble yourselves under the mighty hand of God, that He may exalt you in due time, casting all your care upon Him, for He cares for you."*
   - **1 Peter 5:6-7 (MSG)**

4. *"Honor your father and mother so that you'll live a long time in the land that God, your God, is giving you. No murder, no adultery, no stealing, no lies about your neighbor, and no lusting after your neighbor's house."*
   - **Exodus 20:12-17 (MSG)**

FAMOUS QUOTES:

1. *"We couldn't help getting angry when we were hurt; we had no choice in the matter. We can, however, make a decision about whether we'll allow that anger to turn into rage."*
   - **Brian Jones**

2. *"You shape your future every day through the choices you make. That's sort of a hard one to swallow, isn't it? It would be much easier to say you are a victim of circumstances. Then you don't have to act. Your choices create your reality."*
   - **Jason Harvey**

3. *"When things go wrong, we have one of two choices to make. We can choose to respond with fear, or we can choose to respond with faith."*
   - **Penny Hunt**

TAKEAWAYS:

1. Stress is a trigger that causes us to seek comfort. This is how vices are created. Many vices are destructive to our mind, body, spirit, relationships, and careers.

2. Minimizing stress can minimize or eliminate vices. Seeking comfort in areas that are productive can also eliminate vices. Here are just a few healthy/productive options you can reach for when you are stressed, they all call for ACTION not inaction:

   a. Volunteer to help others in your community
   b. Study the Bible or do research
   c. Meet with your mentor, counselor, or life coach
   d. Write a book about your life and how you overcame adversity
   e. Paint or draw
   f. Exercise/Play sports

3. We all experience stress and we all reach for something to comfort us. Don't spend time judging others for their vices, simply work on your own vice, then lovingly reach out to HELP others with theirs.

4. Chapter 2 is not meant to blame our parents or anyone else for how our life has turned out to this point, but it is meant to help you figure out WHY you are making certain decisions and to help you understand that YOU can make better choices if you focus on your future and remove negative emotions of your past.

5. If you are having problems sleeping or if you wake up between 2:30 – 3:00 AM two to three times weekly, this is an indicator that something is bothering you. You may also experience this if you are excited about some event in your future.

6. Emotional pain is triggered by our senses (i.e., seeing, hearing, tasting, touching, or smelling). Once triggered, an emotional reaction follows, causing you to lash out or shut down, displaying negative emotions of anger, sadness, guilt, grief, anxiety, etc.

AFFIRMATIONS: (Recite each morning)

1. I will make great choices starting today, my future depends on me.
2. I will treat everyone with dignity and respect and love them unconditionally.

TIME TO CLIMB:

Exercise 1: VISUALIZATION EXERCISE

Materials needed: A reader (13-years-old or older).

1. If you are in a classroom, break up into groups of two. If not in a classroom setting, ask someone to help you with this exercise.
2. Take turns reading the passage below to each other.
3. Use your most soothing voice for this exercise.
4. If time is a factor, the facilitator can read the passage below to ALL participants at the same time.
5. **Slowly** read the following passage in a soothing, yet serious tone to the participant:

   a. I want you to close your eyes

   b. It is very important that you keep your eyes closed throughout this exercise.

   c. Now, I want you to imagine your life at the age of 35-years-old.

   d. What is your profession? Are you a high school principal, a doctor, a lawyer, a business owner, a community leader, a retired athlete?

   e. What state or country do you reside in?

   f. What type of home do you live in? Is it a ranch style or two-story home or maybe a condo downtown or on the beach?

   g. Now, I want you to imagine yourself standing in front of your home. You should be able to see your home clearly in your mind's eye. I want you to walk up to your home and see your hand opening the front door. As you walk into your home, I want you to go to the left and enter the large kitchen area. The kitchen has a large island with elegant cabinets. The entire space is absolutely beautiful, just like you designed it. Your friends and family are in the kitchen and they are happy to see that you finally made it home. They give you hugs and kisses. As you proceed through the kitchen, you will make a right as you leave your dining room. You walk up to the sliding glass doors and open them. Your favorite cousin is in the pool with her kids and says, "Hello Cousin, thanks for inviting us over, I love your place." You yell back, "It's great seeing you." As you close the sliding glass door, you turn around and your spouse is standing there with your children.

h. What does your spouse look like? Is he/she tall or short? What type of hair does he/she have? How does he/she smell? How does his/her voice sound? What accent or dialect do they use when speaking?

i. How many children do you have? How old are they? How many girls and how many boys do you have?

j. As you walk toward your spouse and children, you reach out to hug them and kiss them. Then you tell them that you will be back shortly.

k. As you walk upstairs and into your home office, you begin to admire your degrees on the wall. You admire your high school diploma where you graduated with honors. You admire your bachelor's and Master's, Degree from two of the top universities in America where you graduated Summa Cum Laude (with the highest distinction) from both schools. You then walk over to take a close look at your Doctorate Degree hanging on the wall. You are extremely proud of this degree because of the hard work it took to achieve this goal.

l. You smile when you look at the "Key to the City" given to you by the mayor for all your community service and advocacy work.

m. As you leave your office and go back downstairs, you decide to walk into your garage. There are three cars in your garage. I want you to slowly walk around the first car. What type of car is it? Is it a mini-van, a Honda, Mercedes, Bentley? As you move to the second car, take your time as you walk around it. What type of car is it? Then move on to the third car. The third car is a sporty convertible. Open the driver's door and get behind the wheel, let the top down, and lift up the garage door. Drive out of the garage and go into your office for a quick meeting with your staff.

n. When you arrive at the office, go in and let everyone know that they can have the rest of the day off and to enjoy their holiday weekend. Get back into your convertible and head home. Park in the driveway, get out of the car, and admire your home, think of your wonderful family, and the life you have built.

o. Now, open your eyes.

"Although being in an emotional hole is very different from being mentally ill, if left unresolved, emotional illness very often leads to self-sabotage which can further lead to mental and physical illness."

- Roderick Cunningham

LET'S FIX IT

"Turn your wounds into wisdom."　　— Oprah Winfrey

The Five (5) Ways to Conquer Your Life and CLIMB Out of the Emotional Hole

Table 4-1

	Forgiveness	Unfortunately, this is the hardest one for most people to do, but it is the most effective. Forgiveness is for you and your best interest and not for the other person. Here is an effective way for you to forgive someone and remove negative emotions that surface at the thought of that person: 1. Write down the names of everyone who has ever hurt you in your entire life, even if you feel as though you have forgiven them, or you feel the situation is no longer relevant. 2. Write each person a letter in your own handwriting. *(Sample letters can be found in "Success Tools for Your Future", Tool #3, in this workbook)*
	Counseling	Seek out a Life Coach, Behavioral Health Counselor, Spiritual Counselor, Drug/Alcohol Counselor, or Group Counselor.
	Purpose: *Find It and Live It!*	Purpose involves helping others. How is someone else's life better because you lived?
	Journaling: *Share your story,* *Drawing and* *painting*	- Write a song, a poem, a book, or even a movie about your life, your struggles, and the things you think about daily. - Speak to community groups to help others with similar struggles. - Drawing and painting is also a form of therapy that can help you clear your mind of negative emotions.
	Spiritual *Development*	- Spirituality builds faith – Faith fuels every area of your life. - No matter your belief system, study the spiritual book of your faith and let it be your guide. Be specific in your studies. - Replace your vices with your studies. (For example, instead of drinking when you are stressed, study your religion)

Check all of the above that you are willing to do to climb out of your emotional hole.

The list above represents the core ideas of this book. This list was derived from face-to-face mentoring/coaching of over 9,000 people over a four-year period and also from my own emotional hole I faced as a teenager and again at the age of forty-six, when my mother passed away suddenly.

Are you willing to take the first step to change your life? Do you know that the people who have taken the steps laid out in Table 4-1 have seen a positive change in their emotional well-being, which leads to better grades, better relationships, and many times positive career success? Go to our website for specific testimonials (www.chiefempowerment.com). Are you willing to do what it takes to change your life as well? Change takes ACTION.

In order for me to get my life together, I had to do all five of the steps to truly live a life of peace, blessings, and purpose. I feel totally at peace with my MIND, BODY, and SPIRIT. My relationships with God, my wife and children, my friends, my community, etc. are stronger than ever. My wife tells me that I am kind, patient, and understanding, most of the time. Those are new descriptions of my personality that were not used during the first twenty years of marriage.

Distractors

The list below highlights choices we often make to distract us from the real issue of what's bothering us. Although helpful, it is not a fix.

Table 4-2

Joining a church	Practicing generosity	Joining the military
Purchasing a pet	Joining a fraternity/sorority	Taking anti-depressants
Joining a Sports Team (HS/ College/ Pro)	Becoming a community volunteer	Becoming a Shopaholic
Becoming a workaholic	Becoming a runner	Becoming a bodybuilder

These practices mask the pain, but it does not stop the pain. For example, a college or professional athlete may stop playing sports due to an injury but starts to use drugs or start to drink heavily because they are still in an emotional hole from something that happened when they were ten-years-old. Many would attribute the injury and loss of potential wealth as the factor that led to drug and alcohol use, but the real issue is the twenty-year incarceration of their biological father, or the death of their mother when they were just ten-years-old.

If I were coaching this athlete as a life/empowerment coach, I would use Neurolinguistics Programming (NLP)[05] techniques first to help them confront their childhood hurt, pain, or trauma (see Table 4-4). After confronting their past (i.e., an incarcerated father, death of a parent, a verbally, sexually, or physically abusive family member, etc.), then we would confront the lost dream of succeeding in professional sports. Many times, the anger of getting injured may be focused toward the team doctor or coaches for not waiting on the physical injury to heal in order for the player to return to play the sport. If the player does not recognize the emotional hole that they are in, they may start to act out. Unfortunately, we witness the acting out because it is played out often in the news or on social media when a college or professional athlete gets arrested for drinking and driving, domestic violence, drug use, emotional outbursts of anger in public, etc.

Keep in mind that people who shut out (introverts) don't normally get in trouble with the law, but their pain is displayed at home, behind closed doors, and is well known by their immediate family members. The emotional hole for them may lead to domestic violence by verbally and/or physically abusing their spouse and/or children, getting drunk at home and passing out in front of the television, or some just don't communicate very well with their spouse and/or their children and ignore their needs. Some introverts communicate better at work with their co-workers and employees, then at home with family.

QUESTIONS:

1. If I paid you $1 million to STOP using drugs or physically abusing your loved ones, would you do it?
   YES, OF COURSE | NO, I DO WHAT I WANT | IT DEPENDS

   Although this sounds like a simple but interesting question, some professional athletes are faced with this situation daily. If some of them can't stay drug-free or incident-free to keep their million-dollar contracts with their teams and their corporate sponsors, what type of childhood trauma might they have faced that put them in such a deep emotional hole that they are willing to lose millions to seek comfort from drugs or to display uncontrollable anger? My purpose is not to single out athletes because we have other famous people who experience emotional challenges and end up canceling concerts, losing fans, being fired from their television shows, walking off movie sets, going through multiple divorces, in and out of substance abuse clinics, etc. I am addressing famous people because, although it is unfortunate that their lives play out in the media, there is something to learn from it. It is not about pointing fingers at them, but truly empathizing with every human being that may be in an emotional hole.

No matter how rich, famous, popular, or important you may be, if you are fortunate to live a long life, the events of life WILL put you in an emotional hole at some point, and you have to have the proper tools to climb out and climb out fast.

2. The Five (5) Ways to Conquer Your Life is a proven, life-changing system that works. Why do you think people may hesitate to put them into action?

_____

_____

_____

3. Most people believe that when you FORGIVE someone, you are freeing them of their own responsibility to change their behavior and that they owe you an apology before you can forgive them. Many people feel that the person who hurt them should say that they are sorry, they should understand why you are hurt, and you want to know that they will never hurt you again.

   a. What if that apology never comes? If it never comes, do you think that you can still FORGIVE everyone that has ever hurt you physically, sexually, or emotionally?   YES | NO | MAYBE

   b. Should you live your life in emotional pain while you wait on an apology?
      YES | NO | I'M GOOD, I DON'T CARE

   c. Should anyone have that kind of power over your life?
      YES | NO | MAYBE

4. Do you think the person that hurt you is in a deep emotional hole themselves and may not even know it, causing them to hurt others?   YES | NO | POSSIBLY

5. You could be responsible for changing the life of a friend or family member by putting this book in their hands. Who do you know that is in an emotional hole and need these tools right now?

Friend 1: _____ Friend 2: _____

Family Member 1: _____Family Member 2: _____

6. Who do you know that is currently in a Juvenile Detention Center or in jail right now for acting out or was recently released?

_____

_____

7. Who do you know that had a significant death in their family as a young person or teenager (loss of a parent, sibling, friend, child, etc.)?

_____

8. What adult do you know that recently divorced, lost their spouse, lost their child, lost their parent, lost their favorite aunt/uncle, lost a sibling, lost their best friend, etc?

_____

_____

The reason for the eight (8) questions above is for us to start to look at the people around us with empathetic hearts and attempt to understand their mindset and to help them develop a healthy mind. We are all doing the best we can with tools of life that we have been given. Can you imagine if your entire family had a HEALTHY MIND, BODY, and SPIRIT? How would that affect your life and the lives of the people you love? Could a healthy MIND, BODY, and SPIRIT affect an entire community?

Healthy Mind = Living in an abundance of joy and happiness with the ability to manage negative emotions and focus on positive emotions.

Healthy Body = Wake up daily revitalized with no pain or disease in your body

Healthy Spirit = You live with inner peace and you are in peace and harmony with God and all humans

We can look out for one another and recognize key words that people use that let us know that they may be in an emotional hole. We can get them the tools they need to help them. Just hand them this book and tell them that it changed so many people's lives and that it will change theirs too. That's all you have to do. Don't say things like, "You are in a hole," "You're crazy," "You need Jesus," "What the heck is wrong with you?" or "Are you still talking about that? You need to let that go." Just say, "I have an awesome book that has helped me to change my life. You have got to check it out."

SPIRITUAL REFERENCES:

Forgive and you shall be forgiven
1. *"And whenever you stand praying, if you have anything against anyone, forgive him, that your Father in heaven may also forgive you your trespasses. But if you do not forgive, neither will your Father in heaven forgive your trespasses."*
    - **Mark 11:25-26 (NKJV)**

Forgiveness never stops
2. *"Then Peter came to Him and said, "Lord, how often shall my brother sin against me, and I forgive him? Up to seven times?" Jesus said to him, "I do not say to you, up to seven times, but up to seventy times seven."*
    - **Matthew 18:21-22 (NKJV)**

Get wise counsel
3. *"Without good direction, people lose their way; the more wise **counsel** you follow, the better your chances."*
    - **Proverbs 11:14 (MSG)**

4. *"Take good counsel and accept correction – that's the way to live wisely and well."*
    - **Proverbs 19:20 (MSG)**

FAMOUS QUOTES:

1. *"I believe forgiveness is the best form of love in any relationship. It takes a strong person to say they're sorry and an even stronger person to forgive."*
    - **Yolanda Hadid**

2. *"Darkness cannot drive out darkness; only light can do that. Hate cannot drive out hate; only love can do that."*
   - **Martin Luther King, Jr.**

3. *"The best way to not feel hopeless is to get up and do something. Don't wait for good things to happen to you. If you go out and make some good things happen, you will fill the world with hope, you will fill yourself with hope."*
   - **Barack Obama**

TAKEAWAYS:

1. Although forgiveness is hard, it is very necessary to live an empowered life.

2. YOU have the power to change your life. You must decide that you want to be happy 90% of the time, instead of 40%.

3. Sports (playing or watching), pets, shopping, running, bodybuilding, and reading are great ways to relieve stress in your life, but those things do not fix a broken heart and move you out of the emotional hole. You must start on the path of a healthy mind, body, and spirit by using **The Five (5) Ways to Conquer Your Life and CLIMB Out of the Emotional Hole**.

4. If you live long enough, you WILL go into an emotional hole because someone you love will pass away, you may get your heart broken by someone you love, and/or you may find yourself at odds with your parents.

AFFIRMATIONS: (Recite each morning)

1. I will live a prosperous life.
2. I will speak with my mentor weekly.

TIME TO CLIMB:

Exercise 1: UNDERSTANDING EMOTIONS

Materials needed: Inside Out DVD or device to project the movie from your iOS device.

Watch the animated film about emotional health in teenagers called "Inside Out":

Inside Out (2015)

Directed by Pete Docter/Ronne Del Carmen [PG]

Currently found on Apple iTunes for $3.99 to Rent and $14.99 to purchase

----

Exercise2: WHICH ACTION WILL YOU TAKE

Materials needed: Pen

Decide which, if not all, of the 5 **ACTION** steps you are willing to take to **CHANGE** your life. Check all that you are willing to put into action.

The Five (5) Ways to Conquer
Your Life and Climb Out of the Emotional Hole

	Forgiveness	Forgiveness is for YOU and not for the other person.
	Counseling	Seek out a Professional/Spiritual Counselor or Life Coach.
	Purpose: *Find It and Live It!*	Find your purpose in helping others.
	Journaling: *Sharing your story, Drawing/painting*	- Write a song, a poem, a book, or even a movie about your life, your struggles, and the things you think about daily. - Speak to community groups - Drawing and/or painting
	Spiritual Development	- Spirituality builds faith – Faith fuels every area of your life - Replace your vices with your studies. (For example, instead of drinking when you are stressed, study your religion)

"If you don't design your own life plan, chances are you'll fall into someone else's plan. And guess what they have planned for you? Not much."

— Jim Rohn

Chapter 5

FORGIVENESS

"True forgiveness is when you can say, "Thank you for that experience."

- *Oprah Winfrey*

We must forgive everyone who has ever hurt or offended us in any way. I currently coach/mentor 40+ youth and eight adults weekly. Forgiveness is their most difficult action to take. Some actually get angry when I suggest it. I get responses like, "Nope, can't do it, so what is the #2 way to climb out of my emotional hole," or "They really hurt me." Others may say, "You can forgive, but you can't forget." My response to that comment is, "Who told you that? Did you learn that from a person who became comfortable living in their own emotional hole? How happy is the person who taught you that? Do they live in victory? I'm not asking you to forget, I just want you to remove the **negative emotions** that are attached to the thought or memory of that terrible event. Unforgiveness is not serving your life well… no matter what someone has done to you." My clients' response is normally, "But you just don't understand what they did to me."

Here's my Top 5 reasons why my clients find it hard to forgive:

1. Biological mother/father: Broken relationship

   a. Here are a few examples:
   b. Feeling abandoned as a child
   c. Haven't spoken in months or years
   d. Given up for adoption
   e. Cheating parents
   f. Although present, not "actively" involved in their lives or school activities
   g. Rarely expressed love or that they are proud
   h. Parent speaks negatively about each other
   i. Physically, verbally, or sexually abusive
   j. Broken promises to visit, send gifts or send money
   k. Doesn't return phone calls
   l. Not enough attention, too many kids in the home
   m. Parent who committed suicide

	n. Terminally ill parent, limiting activity with their children o. Parents who spoke negative things over their lives
	2. Death of a loved one (i.e., sibling, parent, grandparent, friend, uncle, aunt, cousin, significant other, etc.)
	3. Inappropriate touching Many of my clients were touched inappropriately as a child by an uncle, sibling, step-parent, grandparent, cousin, neighborhood teenager, church member, or family friend. Also, after telling the parent, the parent either did not believe them, blamed them, or told them not to report the incident. They never got resolution to the incident.
	4. Involves a threat to their basic needs (food, clothing, and shelter). Some clients are still hurting from being cut from their college sports team because they had dreams of playing professional sports or they lost their college scholarship, affecting their future earning potential. Also, if fired from a job, they are still angry at their boss because their ability to provide food, clothing, and shelter for themselves and their family had been threatened.
	5. Dishonest significant other Some clients have a hard time forgiving an ex-boyfriend/girlfriend or spouse because they cheated with another person, lacks integrity, abused drugs/alcohol, or was verbally/mentally abusive.

Holding on to unforgiveness can cause undue stress which can cause all kinds of sickness in our bodies later in life. Many times, the person who offended you didn't know they offended you, didn't care that they offended you or didn't mean to offend you. The best way to forgive them is to call them or meet with them to forgive them. Many times, it is hard to face people who have hurt you or they may have passed away, so writing a letter is the next best way. When writing a letter, be sure to follow the sample letter instructions precisely in **Tool #3 in "Success Tools for Your Future."**

CARL

"Carl, grab your backpack, your dad is taking you to school this morning," said Jennifer as Carl was hurrying through his breakfast about to head to the car. "Cool, I love it when dad takes me to school. I can tell him all about how I won the free throw shootout in school," said Carl. Carl is your typical energetic fourth grader. He and his father Craig have a great relationship. They shoot hoops together, talk about sports, go for ice cream every weekend, do homework, and just truly enjoy each other's company.

One day, Carl's mom Jennifer picked him up from school early. She had a very concerned look on her face. Carl said, "Mom, is everything OK. Where is dad? He was supposed to pick me up today." Jennifer began wiping away tears from her face as she listened to Carl. "Son, your father collapsed this morning at work and was rushed to the hospital. I've been at the hospital most of the morning and now your father is resting."

"Mom, you are scaring me, what happened to dad? Is he going to be OK?" said Carl. When they arrive to the hospital, Carl jumped out quickly and grabbed Jennifer to rush her into the hospital to show him where his dad was. When they arrived at the room, Carl ran over and hugged his dad around the stomach area because he had so many machines attached to him. Craig looked up at Jennifer and said, "Thanks for bringing my son."

Over the next few days, Carl refused to go to school. He told his mom that he could do his school work at the hospital. "I want to stay with dad," said Carl. After three days of being in the hospital, the doctors entered the room to speak with Jennifer. "Your husband is really sick," said Dr. Brown. "He has an aggressive form of kidney cancer and unfortunately, it is already in Stage Four and it has spread into multiple areas of his body." "What does this mean," Jennifer asked. "Your husband is only thirty-eight-years-old, and we are going to try to do everything we can to save him, but you need to start getting your affairs in order," said Dr. Brown. "What are you saying to me, are you freaking kidding me, are you saying that my husband is going to die," said Jennifer. "No, no, no, no, no, this cannot be happening right now. We have a great life together. We have a future planned together," said Jennifer as she burst into tears. Jennifer's sister arrived and immediately rushed over to console her. The doctors walked away.

Craig began chemotherapy and other Cancer treatments, but his body rejected it and he began to deteriorate very quickly. Within twenty-eight days of entering the hospital, Craig passed away peacefully in his sleep. Craig and Jennifer's family and friends were by his bed side. Jennifer asked that everyone clear the room so that she could have a private last moment with her husband. Jennifer spent forty-five minutes alone saying her goodbyes to her husband. When Jennifer exited the hospital room, her father had just picked up Carl from school and had brought him to the hospital. Carl and his grandfather exited the elevator and began to walk toward his dad's room. Carl saw the look on his mother's face as she stood in the hallway and fell to his knees in tears. Jennifer rushed over to pick him up from the floor. They were both crying uncontrollably. "I want my dad, I want my dad back," said Carl. "I know sweetheart, I know," said Jennifer. Craig's mother and father, and Jennifer's mother and father all walk over to embrace Jennifer and Carl. Suddenly, Carl feels smothered and yells, "Get away from me," as he broke loose and ran down the hall toward the elevator. His grandfather patiently walked toward him, and Carl said, "Don't touch me. Get away." His grandfather patiently stood there and watched him. Carl fell to his knees slowly and said, "Why did this have to happen to my dad? I don't understand." Carl's grandfather dropped to one knee, and hugged Carl while still on the ground and said, "I love you grandson. I'm here for you. Whatever you need, I'm here for you."

One year after his father's death, Carl's demeanor had changed considerably. He lost his interest in basketball, he shut others out, he got angry quickly, and didn't want anyone to touch him or his things. His grades dropped, he played video games for four hours every night, and didn't quite know how to talk to anyone about his feelings. He didn't want to talk to his mother because she still cried herself to sleep every night. Without Craig's income, Jennifer had to sell the house and move into an apartment. Craig's small insurance policy offered at work was only enough to keep them in the home for twelve months.

At the end of the sixth-grade school year, Carl and other boys in his class attended a neighborhood sleepover at Bobby's house. That night at the sleepover, the boys were eating hot dogs, watching comic movies, laughing, and talking about who is the best 3-point shooter at their school. When the boys fell asleep around 11:00 pm, Bobby's sixteen-year-old brother Will, came and woke up four of the boys and told them to follow him. The boys, including Carl, quietly got up and followed Will into the garage. Will offered the boys marijuana. Two of the boys took it right away, but Carl was very hesitant. His buddies said, "come on Carl, it will make you feel good bro." Carl slowly put the marijuana to his lips and inhaled. They all started laughing and began to pass multiple marijuana cigarettes between each other for about an hour. Will began to massage Carl on his shoulders and said, "We are brothers for life. We have to look out for each other." The younger boys were happy to be around Will because he was in high school and was very popular. Will told the other boys to quietly go back in the house, but he kept Carl back in the garage with him. Will touched Carl in very inappropriate ways and Carl was shocked, scared, and didn't know what he should do. He froze. He couldn't believe this was happening to him. After one hour of being alone in the garage with Will, Carl went back into the house, got into his sleeping bag, and quietly cried all night.

The next morning when Jennifer picked Carl up from the sleepover, Carl was just very quiet. Jennifer said, "Did you have a good time, Son." Carl responded by saying, "It was fine." "Just fine," she asked. "Yes, mom, it was fine," he said. "I'm just ready to go home and go to sleep. I don't feel well," Carl said. "Did anything happen, are you OK," asked Jennifer. Carl thought for a moment and was about to reveal to his mother what happened, but then he got scared, felt ashamed, and embarrassed. He said, "Mom, everything is fine. Can we go now?" Jennifer knew something was wrong, but figured that Carl was just missing his father.

When summertime came, Carl went into a deeper shell than ever before. He was having a hard time sleeping. He awoke every night around 3:00 am and he would just stare at the ceiling. He hardly ever came out of his room. During the summer, he would play video games for eight-hours-a-day. When school started back, Carl was a 7th grader in middle school. He started getting into trouble almost immediately. He would talk back to teachers and he started hanging out with kids who were making really bad decisions. He started smoking marijuana often with his friends.

It was a rainy day in September in Florida. Mrs. Gray's classroom was working quietly on an assignment. Suddenly, a desk flipped over in the back of the class and students began to scatter immediately. Mrs. Gray got on the two-way radio and calls for faculty assistance. Carl was standing in the back of the room in anger. He had a blank stare and was breathing heavily. All the other kids were heading out of the door and into the hallway. Mr. Grant pushed through the kids to enter the room. "Carl, I need you to come with me." Carl didn't move. He yelled, "Carl, did you hear me!?" Carl looked up as to come out of a daze. "What?" Carl asked. "Come on, let's go," said Mr. Grant. Carl walked out of the classroom with his head down as Mr. Grant followed behind him.

As Mr. Grant was walking with Carl to the office, he asked, "What is wrong with you? Why did you flip over your desk? What were you thinking?" Carl looked at Mr. Grant with this blank stare and shrugged his shoulder as if to say, "I did what? I don't remember what I did or why I did it."

Cindy was a student in the classroom. As the other students were putting the room back together, she approached the teacher and told her that Justin was picking on Carl. He was sitting behind him calling him names. "Well, what did Justin say exactly," asked Mrs. Gray. He said, "Man, why are you so stupid? You don't know anything. You can't beat me in basketball." Mrs. Gray said, "Carl got that mad from that." "No ma'am," said Cindy. Carl flipped the desk as soon as Justin said, "You're a punk, you're gay." "But Cindy, I hear the boys saying that to each other all of the time at this school. I try to step in when I hear it," said Mrs. Gray. "I wonder why those words are so offensive to Carl," said Mrs. Gray.

When Carl got to the principal's office, he sat outside of the door waiting to talk to him. Principal Davis said, "Carl what happened?" "I don't know, they say I flipped over my desk. I can't remember anything," said Carl. "I just blacked out and all I remember is Mr. Grant yelling at me to leave the classroom," said Carl. "Do you black out often?" asked Principal Davis. "I don't know," said Carl.

Principal Davis scheduled an evaluation with the school and district psychologist to evaluate Carl. Principal Davis then called Carl's mother, Jennifer, to come to the school to have a conversation about her son. During the third visit with the school appointed psychologist, Carl revealed that he had been molested by Will six months prior. There was a full investigation launched, and by the end of the 7th grade school year, Will had been arrested, sentenced to two years in detention, and had to register as a sex-offender. There were three other victims who also came forward during Will's trial.

After the trial, Carl began to feel a lot better. He felt as though he was finally heard and that someone cared about him. Carl couldn't help but get angry at his father though. He told the psychiatrist, "If my dad was here, none of this would have ever happened."

Carl started to practice basketball more often. He would go up to the gym every day for hours. He tried out for the junior varsity team at his high school and made the team. Carl was still secretly smoking marijuana. He was also on medication for bi-polar disorder and visited his psychologist about every three months.

Carl started dating Samantha, one of the school's cheerleaders, in his 11th grade year. Samantha and Carl had a lot in common. Samantha's father also passed away when she was in elementary school and she too smoked marijuana. Samantha was a very good listener. Carl and Samantha talked for two hours each and every day. Samantha really believed in Carl and encouraged him to follow his dreams. Whenever Carl got angry, he called Samantha and she would calm him down every time.

Carl was struggling with manhood and wondered to himself if he was a man yet. He no longer had a father to teach him what manhood was, and his mother could not teach a man how to be a man. As he looked around his neighborhood and at his cousins, he noticed that everyone considered them men because they all had children. Carl also struggles with the image of what happened to him in Will's garage back when he was just eleven years old. Carl often told Samantha that he wanted to marry her after high school graduation. Carl and Samantha started having sexual relations and Carl got Samantha pregnant on purpose so that he could have a child, figuring people would finally see him and treat him as a man.

In Carl's senior year of high school, he became a father. He had to quit the basketball team and get a job after school to support his child. He went to work from 4-8 pm on school nights and sixteen hours on the weekend, putting in thirty-six hours-a-week at two different jobs. He rode his bicycle to work. The more stressed he got from school, homework, two jobs, and raising a son, the more marijuana he smoked, although he told his mother that he was going to have to stop smoking once the baby came. Samantha had already stopped once she got pregnant, but Carl's smoking got worse. About a month before high school graduation, Carl and Samantha broke up for good after Carl was fired from one of his jobs because he was caught kissing another girl at work in the breakroom. Someone at work had taken a picture of them kissing and put it all over social media.

After Samantha broke up with him, Carl felt as though he had lost his best friend. He'd lost the person who cared about him the most. He'd lost the person that was there for him, no matter what. He didn't realize how much he depended on Samantha to be there for him, until he lost her. He didn't realize how much she had listened to him and how much he had leaned on her for support. She was his rock and now she was gone.

Whenever Carl picked up his son for the weekend, Samantha would remain in her room and would not come out. Samantha's mother would hand the baby to Carl. Samantha refused to see him or take his calls for almost a year. She started quietly dating a guy from her job. Once Carl found out, he started calling and texting Samantha to say how much he hated her. She ignored him.

Carl was fired from his other job after failing a random drug test of all their employees. He got depressed and just laid around the house for months, playing video games all day. His mom got tired of seeing her son do nothing. She said, "You have three weeks to find a job, go to the Job Corps, or join the military. All I know is that you can't live here and not work." He continued to play the video game. She said, "Boy do you hear me!?" He said, "Yes mom, I hear you."

Two weeks later, Carl enrolled in the Job Corps to take a trade. He decided to get certified as a plumber because he'd heard that they make good money. The Job Corps allows their students to live on-campus, giving Carl the opportunity to move out of his mother's home.

The Job Corps employed Mr. Jarvis, a certified life coach, on staff, and one-day Carl met him while walking to lunch. "What do you do here Sir," asked Carl. "I'm a life coach. I help people live an amazing life," said Mr. Jarvis. "How does that work?" asked Carl. "I help you find balance in your life, help you design a more powerful future, and I help you overcome negative thoughts and emotions that you may deal with on a daily basis. We all have something that we deal with in our minds, normally tied to our past. I help you remove the negative emotions associated with that past," said Mr. Jarvis. "Would you like to stop by my office for a visit?" he asked. Carl said, "Nope, I'm good. No problems here." Mr. Jarvis responded by saying, "Do you ever get sad or angry? How many times can I push your emotional buttons before I will see sadness or anger emerge?" Carl responded by saying, "It depends on who is pushing my emotional buttons. If it is someone in my family, my friends, or my ex-girlfriend, then I can go from 0-100 in about two seconds. I get angry really fast. But, so does everyone." "No Carl," said Mr. Jarvis, "Everyone does not have anger problems. People have a tendency to make their reality everyone else's reality because it makes them feel better about their own life struggles. Wouldn't you like to be happy 90% of the time instead of 40% of the time? You have the power within you to live your best life NOW, but you have to be taught how to do that," said Mr. Jarvis. Carl said, "Wow, you are deep, sir. Can I come today after class?" "Sure. I will see you at 3:30 today," said Mr. Jarvis.

When Carl met with Mr. Jarvis, he told his life's story within the first hour of the session. Mr. Jarvis talked to Carl about the five ways to climb out of the psychological hole and he started with the first step, forgiveness. He asked Carl to write down the names of everyone that has ever hurt him in his entire life. Carl wrote down six names, to include his mother for kicking him out of the house and abandoning him, his father for dying on him, Will, for touching him, Samantha, for leaving him, and both of his previous employers for firing him. Mr. Jarvis stated, "Carl, do you realize that you have let all of these people control your thoughts and your decisions for your life? Only you and God should have control over your mind. I am going to help you learn how to take control over your own mind." Carl said, "I don't let others control me, what are you talking about?" "When you think about the pain that these six people have caused you, what emotions are exhibited from you," said Mr. Jarvis. "Well, when I think about my dad, I get sad. When I think about my mom, I get frustrated. When I think about Will, Samantha, and my old supervisors, I get very angry." "You are making my point Carl. Every time you think about these people and your past, they put you in a very delicate state emotionally. That means that they are now controlling you and your mind. The feeling of sadness and anger also affects your most important relationships... relationships with your son, significant other, mom, friends, and any future employers," said Mr. Jarvis.

That same night, Carl sat down when a pen and paper and wrote letters to all six people on his list. In the letters, he expressed all of his emotions for each person and the fact that they hurt him. He ended each letter with "I forgive myself, I love myself, and I forgive you." After reading each letter three times, he took the letters outside and burned each one. As he watched the words on the paper burn away and disappear, he immediately started to feel lighter. After all the letters were burned, he stood a little taller and more confident. He had a big smile on his face.

During the coaching session the following week, Carl told Mr. Jarvis that he had burned the letters. Mr. Jarvis congratulated Carl and said, "I'm proud of you. How does it feel?" "It feels great. I feel lighter, more at peace," said Carl. Mr. Jarvis said, "There are four parts to the forgiveness exercise. Part one is writing down the names of those that have ever hurt you. Part two is writing the letters of forgiveness, ensuring that you follow the exact instructions. Part three is the burning of the letters. Part four is the creation and daily reading of the gratefulness list." Carl asked, "What is a gratefulness list?" Mr. Jarvis asked, "Well Carl, what are you grateful for?" Carl gave an immediate smile and stated, "I'm grateful for my mom." Mr. Jarvis asked, "What else?" "Well, I am grateful for my son, I am grateful for great health, I am grateful for life, and I am grateful for being at the Job Corps learning a trade." "Great job," said Mr. Jarvis. "See, when you write down a list of things that you are grateful for and review this list every morning, it reminds you to be thankful for what God has given you and to focus on being grateful instead of focusing on negative things or things you don't have. Again, this is a way to ensure you and God are controlling your mind and no one else. Write these things down and review them each morning when you wake up. Also, whenever a negative thought comes to your mind, if you are not coming up with an ACTION to fix what you are thinking about, then that thought is considered an unhealthy thought and it's time to interrupt that thought with your gratefulness list. You can't be happy and angry at the exact same moment, so allow the gratefulness list to put a smile back on your face," said Mr. Jarvis. Carl met with Mr. Jarvis once per week for six months.

Carl is now twenty-four-years-old now and he and a friend have started their own plumbing business. Carl picks his son up from school every day and they go to the basketball court to shoot hoops. After basketball, they stop for ice cream, then he takes his son home to his mother. Carl is engaged to be married and life is good.

QUESTIONS:

1. What are the events that put Carl in an emotional hole?

   _____

   _____

   _____

2. Do you think he was in an emotional hole as a child, adult, or both?
   CHILD | ADULT | BOTH

3. If he was in an emotional hole, do you think his hole was shallow or deep?
   SHALLOW | DEEP | I HAVE NO IDEA

4. Which relationships do you think were affected by his emotional state?
   (Check all that apply)

	The relationship with his son
	The relationship with his significant other (Samantha)
	The relationship with his mom (Jennifer)
	The relationship with his friends
	The relationship with his supervisors

5. What are the events that helped Carl out of his emotional hole?
   (Check all that apply)

	Counseling sessions in middle school
	Will getting sentenced to two years in Juvenile Detention
	Life Coaching sessions with Mr. Jarvis
	Forgiveness
	Getting a trade
	Starting his business
	Playing basketball with his son after school

SPIRITUAL REFERENCES:

We are all God's children
"For you did not receive the spirit of bondage again to fear, but you received the Spirit of adoption by whom we cry out, "Abba, Father." The Spirit Himself bears witness with our spirit that we are children of God, and if children, then heirs—heirs of God and joint heirs with Christ, if indeed we suffer with Him, that we may also be glorified together."
- **Romans 8:15-17 (NKJV)**

FAMOUS QUOTES:

1. *"People are illogical, unreasonable, and self-centered. Love them anyway."*
   - **Kent M. Keith**

2. *"The weak can never forgive. Forgiveness is the attribute of the strong."*
   - **Mahatma Gandhi**

TAKEAWAYS:

1. We will experience many negative events in life that can put us in an emotional hole. There are steps to climbing out of the hole and you were probably never taught them ALL. Once you learn how, you can climb out quickly after life's **next** negative event. If you teach your family how to do the same, you will change generations to come.

2. Don't blame others for how your life turned out. Forgive them, forgive their actions, forgive yourself, and learn from the experience.

3. Past negative events will make you stronger or weaker. Will you choose victory or defeat? Forgiveness puts you in the driver's seat.

AFFIRMATIONS: *(Recite each morning)*

1. I am a forgiver and I live in victory.
2. I will tell my family and anyone who supports me financially that I love them and appreciate them for being in my life.

TIME TO CLIMB:

Exercise 1: FORGIVE EVERYONE

Materials needed: Pen

1. Write down the names of everyone who has ever hurt you in your entire life?

2. Some participants will have a list of three names while others may have ten or more.

_____

_____

_____

_____

_____

_____

_____

_____

_____

_____

_____

_____

_____

Exercise 2: WRITE THEM A LETTER

Materials needed: Notepad and pen

1. It's time to write a letter to EVERYONE you identified in Exercise 1.

2. When writing letters, follow the sample letter instructions precisely in **Tool #3 in "Success Tools for Your Future"**.

3. The letters must have 3 components:

   a. Include all your negative emotions in the letter because this will be the last time these emotions are expressed. Also, write down how you expected this person to treat you.

   b. Include what you have learned from this situation that is positive (even if the only thing that you learned was that you survived, and that the ordeal made you a stronger person).

      1) Did this event make you a kinder, more empathetic person to your friends, siblings, cousins, etc.?
      2) Did this event make you want to be a better parent?
      3) Did this event make you a hard worker?
      4) Did this event make you want to become more successful?
      5) Did this event make you seek out your life's passion where you are always lending a helping hand to other people?
      6) Did this event bring you closer to God or caused you to study his principles?
      7) Did this event cause you to want to do more with your life?

   c. End each letter with "I love myself, I forgive myself, and I forgive you".

4. If you are 18-years-old or older, I suggest that you read the letter three times, then BURN each letter separately. This can be done in the kitchen sink, on the side with the garbage disposal. If you are a minor, then I suggest that you RIP IT UP into tiny little pieces and flush each letter separately down the toilet. It is important to watch the letter as it disappears into the toilet.

"The best years of your life are the ones in which you decide your problems are your own. You do not blame them on your mother, the ecology, or the president. You realize that you control your own destiny."

– Albert Ellis

Chapter 6

COUNSELING

"It lessened some of the suffocating weight I carried by finally opening up to a counselor."

- Jennifer L. Armentrout

The American Counseling Association defines Professional Counseling as a professional relationship that empowers diverse individuals, families, and groups to accomplish mental health, wellness, education, and career goals. Counselors work with clients on strategies to overcome obstacles and personal challenges that they are facing. [04]

Our parents and grandparents are normally our first counselors. They help us figure out who we are and why we do things a certain way. They help us develop educational and career goals and help us figure out what is "normal" and "not-so normal" behavior.

Our school teachers and coaches become our second layer of counselors in our lives. Many times, the counseling we receive from our teachers may conflict with that of our parents. For example, some parents instruct their children to fight back if someone is antagonizing them, while the teacher instructs them to report the incident.

As mentioned in the chapter's opening paragraph, counseling is simply to empower individuals, families, and groups. I have found that culturally speaking, many African-Americans and Hispanics refuse to seek counseling due to the stigma that they assume is attached to counseling or coaching. African-Americans are normally taught by their parents and grandparents that household problems are to remain "in-the-house." They are forbidden to speak of negative family issues. This code of secrecy and distrust of a professional counselor, coach, or spiritual counselor has caused members of the African-American community to live with undue stress and emotional pain that they are forced to suppress for decades.

For some reason, many people feel as though a counselor will tell others what was told to them and somehow embarrass the client. First of all, professional counselors are not allowed to tell anyone what was discussed during a session. Second of all, counselors and coaches hear so many wild stories of inappropriate behaviors that it is unlikely that your life's story will be a surprise to them.

BORIS

"Good Morning Atlanta!"

The over-enthusiastic voice blared from the radio waking Bo out of his sleep. He looked over at it squinting out of one eye, and lazily reached over to turn it off. After a moment, he sat up slowly on the edge of his bed. It was an extremely hot summer morning and he was not in the mood to deal with the world just yet.

He eventually forced himself out of bed and headed over to the bathroom. He wiped his eyes and let out a loud yawn as he stood in front of the mirror. He studied his reflection and eventually made eye contact with it. After a moment, his eyes met the portrait of his brother that was tattooed on his chest. Looking at his tattoo sent his mind back to his sophomore year of high school. It was the first time in his life that he had to navigate through school without his big brother Greg. Greg had gone off to college that year and their father couldn't be prouder of his eldest son. Bo's father was a police officer and never let Bo forget that he wished he was more like Greg.

Mr. Jackson was tough on Bo, but Mrs. Jackson made up for it as much as she could. Bo looked to his mother for any support that he needed, and she was always there to give it. Whether he was sneaking forehead kisses from his mother after a scolding by his father or looking for his mother's support after posting his scholastic awards on the refrigerator that his father never noticed.

In the middle of Bo's sophomore year, his family changed forever. Greg was killed in a car accident on his way home from college. Mr. Jackson started drinking and Mrs. Jackson went into a shell. Bo kept to himself and mourned the loss of his brother all on his own. His father only came home to sleep after a long day at work, followed by many drinks at the bar, and Bo could no longer rely on his mother for support because she needed support herself.

The entire community was devastated by the loss of Greg His funeral was packed with family, everyone from their high school, and his coaches and teammates from his college basketball team.

Bo, who was usually a great student, started to fall behind in his lessons. He spent most of his time cooped up in his room listening to rap music. Eventually he started smoking marijuana because it helped him with the overwhelming sadness that he seemed to feel all the time. By the time Bo graduated, he had left his college dreams behind and opted for culinary school.

The sound of Bo's cell phone snapped him out of his flashback. It was his mother calling as she did almost every morning. He answered and left the phone on speaker as he loaded toothpaste onto his toothbrush.

"Good morning mom" he called out in between brushing. "Good morning sugar. How are you?" she replied. "I'm okay, just surviving and maintaining," said Bo.

After a bit of small talk, Bo asked about his father, not out of concern, but out of pure curiosity. His father had opted for an early retirement out of the police force and had been heavily drinking every day since. His mother told him that nothing had changed much, and they ended their conversation with Bo telling his mother that he loved her and had to get ready for work.

He worked at an upscale resort as a chef's assistant but dreamed of opening his own restaurant. His roommate Chris worked as a server at the same resort and neither of them could afford a car, so they biked to work together. Eventually Bo started to take his dream of owning a restaurant seriously and started taking business courses at the local university. One day after class, Bo was walking to his bike with his head down, focused on picking the perfect playlist for his twenty-minute ride to work. Before he knew it, he had walked right into someone. In shock, he immediately started to apologize and helped the young lady pick up her papers. Bo picked up the papers that he was able to catch with his foot and started to hand them back to her. As her hand met his, he noticed her beauty for the first time.

She wore no makeup, had her hair in a bun, and he was in awe of her.

"I apologize, no one has ever accused me of being graceful. I'm Boris." He said with an actual smile.

"Hi Boris, I'm Tammy." She said, laughing at his joke.

"Since I ran you over, the least I can do is make sure you make it to wherever you're going safely. Do you mind if I walk with you?" He asked.

"I guess not, but my class is just a few feet away." She said nodding to a closed door behind them.

Boris walked Tammy to class and thought about her nonstop for the rest of the night. About a week later Bo noticed Tammy as he was leaving class again. She was headed into the cafeteria, so he threw away the bag of chips he was snacking on, popped in a piece of gum and headed into the cafeteria to find her. He slipped into the same line that she was in hoping that she wouldn't notice him. Once he got his food he walked nonchalantly over to where she was sitting.

"Tammy, right?" he asked, pretending as if it were a chance meeting. "Hi Boris," she replied with a friendly smile. "Do you mind if I join you?" he asked. "Sure, as long as you don't knock the table over," Tammy said as they both laughed.

By the end of their meal, Bo mustered up enough courage to ask Tammy out, and she accepted.

Bo and Tammy saw each other every day since their meal together in the cafeteria. Bo would walk her to class and then rush to work. After about a month of hanging out they decided to officially start dating. As they got to know each other, Tammy opened up about her father leaving her and her mother, and Bo opened up about his brother. He told her how much he missed him and how hard it was living in his shadow while living under their father's roof. Tammy always listened but at times she didn't know what to say, so she would just kiss him on his forehead and tell him that she was there for him. Bo always felt comforted by his mother's forehead kisses and felt that meeting Tammy was fate, so after only forty days of dating, he told her that he loved her. He had never said those words to anyone outside of his family and she had never heard them from a boy. From that point on they were inseparable.

At first, Tammy only spent weekends at Bo's apartment, but eventually she found herself sleeping there almost every night. Bo loved Tammy's company, and everything seemed perfect for a while. After about six months, Bo started to change. He wasn't used to sharing his space and it started to feel overwhelming to him. He started hanging out with Chris and the other guys from work more and more, and he was drinking, and smoking marijuana more than he ever had before. He told Tammy that it helped him not to constantly think about his brother's death and his father's rejection, and that he had more fun with his friends when he was drunk or high. Tammy started to feel as if she was constantly irritating him and that his downward spiral was her fault for not being a good enough girlfriend.

One night, Bo was preparing to go out with his friends and he assured Tammy that he would be back no later than 12:30 am. He did not return until 6:00 am that morning. When he finally stumbled into his room, Tammy was awake and furious. She screamed at the top of her lungs at him, telling him how worried she was and that she shouldn't have to call him a million times without getting an answer. She called him stupid for being so irresponsible. Tammy's words cut through Bo like a knife, he had flashbacks of his father yelling at him and he started to leave the room. Tammy grabbed his arm and apologized for yelling. She pulled him toward her and brought his head to her lips to kiss his forehead.

"I'm sorry Bo. I didn't mean to yell at you. You are the most important person in the world to me and I don't want to lose you. Can I have a kiss?"

Bo was very confused at this moment. He was trying to figure out why Tammy would talk so badly to him, then want to kiss him. Tammy did not want Bo to leave because she remembered the last time her mother screamed at her father, he left the house and never returned, and Tammy did not want that to happen to her and Bo.

A month after their fight, Bo stayed out late partying again with Chris.

After Chris noticed the time, he said "Yo, Bo you might want to call Tammy, you already know she's going flip out on you bro."

"Man, trust me, I've got this, she has daddy issues bro. She will yell, apologize, and ask for a kiss. I'm all good."

Sure enough, Bo was right. He and Tammy continued the same cycle for the next two years. He drank and smoked heavily, went out with Chris every weekend, and argued with Tammy when he came home. Tammy stayed with Bo in hopes that he would one day return to the nice guy that she bumped into in the courtyard on campus. She knew that Bo had the potential to be a great man, because he proved it when they brought their daughter into the world. Bo was a pretty good father to their daughter and did everything he could to make sure her needs were met, but he put no effort into his relationship with Tammy.

After Tammy had their daughter Beatrice, she maintained only one college course and continued to live with Bo. When she and Bo were on good terms, he promised her that he would change, and that one day they would get married. After a while Tammy started to give up on the idea of Bo changing. Instead of waiting up for him when he went out, Bo started to find Tammy and Beatrice sound asleep when he stumbled into the apartment.

Eventually, Tammy realized that Beatrice filled the void that was in her heart for so long. Her daughter brought her so much joy and for the first time she knew what unconditional love felt like. After contemplating week after week, Tammy decided to leave Bo and move back home with her mother and step-father. When Tammy told Bo that she was leaving he begged her to stay.

"Tammy please, I love you, and I love our daughter. Don't do this to me," he said.

"Look Bo, I'm not doing this to you, I'm doing this for our daughter. She doesn't deserve to have a part-time dad who can't even stay sober for twenty-four hours," said Tammy.

"I promise I will change, just don't take her away. You two are the best things that I have in my life and I was stupid to take ya'll for granted," pleaded Bo as his eyes filled with tears.

"I'm sorry Bo, I stayed for over two years hoping that you would change, but it's time for me to put my daughter's needs first. I'll do a video call with you when we land so you can see her and tell her good night."

Tammy kissed Bo on the forehead one last time and walked out with tears in her eyes.

Bo was devastated. He drank to the point that his friends no longer wanted to hang out with him, and just like his sophomore year of high school, he was all alone. One Saturday night, he sat in his living room looking at five empty bottles of whiskey, and an ash tray full of the tail ends of about twenty marijuana joints. At that point, he realized what rock bottom felt like. For the first time since he had started drinking, he genuinely wanted to change, but he didn't know how. At that point, he was visibly depressed, he'd lost fifteen pounds in a month, and barley got any sleep. All he did was go to work and play video games for hours on end. He was written up a few times for smelling like alcohol at work. It was coming out of his pores. When he was drinking, he had a habit of calling Tammy in the middle of the night. He would beg for her to come back and then get angry when she said no. Eventually Tammy stopped answering his calls. She called his mother and told her that Bo really needed help and that she was going to have to cut Beatrice out of his life if he didn't get it.

Eventually it got to the point that Bo only called on holidays and on Beatrice's birthday. He would talk to his daughter and to Tammy for a while, but she always made an excuse to get off the phone and ended the call.

Bo's mother grew more and more worried about him as time passed, so one day she went to visit and have a talk with her son.

They sat on his couch and talked for hours. After she let Bo get all of his emotions and frustrations out, she suggested that he see a counselor.

"No, mom. I am not crazy, and I don't need to be airing my dirty laundry out to a stranger. What could they tell me about my life that I don't already know? Besides, I'm twenty-one years-old, it's too late, I'm already stuck in my ways." he said as he sank into the couch.

"Sugar I know you're not crazy, you're far from it. Just take a second to think son, do you remember how low I was when we lost Greg? Do you think I just up and pulled myself out of that depression one day? No baby, I got help, I knew if I didn't my whole life would be in shambles. Your father would have driven me even crazier with his drinking and who knows where I would have ended up. I know what's down this path of drinking and doing drugs son, and I do not want that life for you. Even very successful people seek counseling as they can give you ideas on how to sleep better at night, techniques to work through how you view your problems, and techniques on how to build a better future," she said.

Bo took his mother's words into consideration but still decided that counseling wasn't for him. A few months after Beatrice's third birthday, Tammy married her new boyfriend. Tammy's new husband was very fond of Beatrice and wanted to adopt her. Bo laughed at Tammy when she tried to get him to sign over his parental rights. He told her that would never happen, and that Beatrice was his daughter, and no one would ever take that away from him. Tammy told Bo that Beatrice had a new father figure, one that was a good influence and that she didn't need Bo anymore. She told Bo that he was a distraction and not to call anymore. Bo got angry and yelled at Tammy. She hung up the phone and never answered his calls again.

When Bo was twenty-eight, he met a nice woman named Pamela and after a few years of dating, they got married. Although they had their good times, Bo was still depressed, he still drank, smoked marijuana, and played video games for hours. Eventually Bo and Pamela had two kids of their own; a son, Boris Jr., and a daughter Brittany. After five years of marriage Bo and Pamela got a divorce.

After his divorce, Bo's friends and family urged him to seek counseling, but it took another two years for him to finally seek help. He started going to counseling sessions every week for six months. His counselor, Dr. Samuels, helped him to forgive his father for not accepting him for who he is, forgive Tammy for leaving him, face the passing of his brother and finally deal with the pain that had been crippling him for so many years. Dr. Samuels also helped Bo start to sleep better and gave him tips on how to build strength in the most important relationships in his life... his relationships with his parents, children, significant other, friends, and his employer.

Bo told Dr. Samuels about Beatrice who was then fourteen-years old. Dr. Samuels explained that Beatrice was at a critical age and she needed to know that her father loves her and is proud of her. Dr. Samuels acknowledged that facing Beatrice would be difficult, but that it was also critical.

That night Bo went home and called his younger children and told them that he loved them, they meant the world to him, and that he would always be proud of them. He wanted to talk to Tammy before he reached out to Beatrice, so he looked her up on social media and there she was. The profile picture showed her, her husband, Beatrice, and two more children all dressed in white and smiling from ear-to-ear. Bo mustered up the courage and sent her a message. He explained that he was getting counseling and he apologized for everything that he put her and their daughter through over the years. He told her that he knew Beatrice was missing a piece of herself because she had no relationship with her father and he wanted to take steps to change that. He said that he knew firsthand what it feels like to not have a relationship with your biological father. He mentioned how he was sure that Tammy's husband was a great role model for his daughter, but that his daughter still needed to know that her biological father loves her and is proud of her.

After two days Tammy responded. She had asked Beatrice if she wanted to hear from Bo and Beatrice said that she did. Bo opened a social media message from Tammy that explained that this would be Bo's last chance to be a part of his daughter's life and she gave him Beatrice's cell phone number. He read the message about ten times before he decided that he was ready to make the call.

For the first time in a very long time, Bo was sober. He had started attending AA meetings and steadily continued his sessions with Dr. Samuels.

He dialed his daughter's number and was shocked when she answered the phone, she sounded so much like her mother, and she sounded very mature.

"Hello, dad, is this you?" she asked

"Hi baby girl, yea, it's your dad."

Beatrice asked her father if he loved her and why he never called. Bo assured her that he was always thinking of her and apologized for his absence.

"Baby girl, I think the world of you and I'm asking for a second chance. I love you and I am proud to be your father. It would mean everything to me if you would forgive me and give me the chance to get to know you."

Beatrice agreed to forgive her father and they talked for hours that night. Bo told Beatrice about her little sisters and they have spoken four or five times a week ever since. Bo always made sure that Beatrice came to see him in the summers and he spent more time with his younger children as well.

He was eventually able to forgive his father and he and his two younger children started eating dinner at his parent's house every Sunday. He met a wonderful woman named Eva and they started dating. They decided to take things slowly, but after dating for three years they got married.

When Beatrice turned eighteen, she decided to attend the same college her mother had attended to be closer to her father. When she moved into her dorm room, Tammy, her step-father Dennis, and Bo and Eva, all helped her get settled in. Beatrice started to attend Sunday dinners at her grandparents' house and she and her younger siblings grew incredibly close and they started to look to her for advice.

At forty-years-old, Bo could finally say he was happy, he was working on a business plan for his restaurant, and life was finally good.

QUESTIONS:

1. Do you think Bo was heartbroken and in an emotional hole as a child, adult, or both?
   CHILD | ADULT | BOTH

2. Which event do you think pushed Bo deeper in his hole?

	His father not being proud of him the same way he was proud of his big brother (Greg)
	The death of Greg
	Not communicating often with his father since the age of 16
	Tammy and Beatrice walking out on him
	His divorce from Pamela and her taking his two kids

3. Once Tammy left, Bo really began to sink deeper into his emotional hole. Which relationships do you think were affected by Bo's actions while in his early 20's?

	The relationship with his child (Beatrice)
	The relationship with his significant other (Tammy)
	The relationship with his parents (dad)
	The relationship with his friends (Chris)
	The relationship with his employer at the resort

4. Many times, we choose vices (see Table 1-1) that appear normal because we saw others in our family with the same vice or it is a vice that is most acceptable in our particular community. In other words, my dad drank, so I drank. My mom smoked marijuana, so it's okay for me to smoke. My friends are having sex, so I want to have sex. I see my mom stealing, so its fine for me to steal. Those familiar family vices are considered normal and most accepted by parents, siblings, uncles, aunts,

cousins, etc. Many times, these vices are considered "no big deal". Which vice do you think Bo picked up from his mother or father?

	Alcohol		Sexual promiscuity
	Gambling		Pornography
	Marijuana		Cigarettes

5. Bo waited until his late thirties to seek counseling. Do you think his life could have been better had he sought counseling as a teenager or in his early twenties?
    YES | NO | I'M NOT SURE

6. If Bo's family would have sought family counseling after Greg's death, could they have built a stronger family bond of love and support for each other?
    YES | NO | I'M NOT SURE

7. If Bo had experienced a stronger family bond of love and support, could he have been a better boyfriend, friend, father, employee, son, etc.?
    YES | NO | I'M NOT SURE

SPIRITUAL REFERENCES:

Lust and Alcohol
1. *"Let us walk properly, as in the day, not in revelry and drunkenness, not in lewdness and lust, not in strife and envy. But put on the Lord Jesus Christ, and make no provision for the flesh, to fulfill its lusts."*
    -   **Romans 13:13-14 (NKJV)**

Offense never ends, so forgiveness never ends
2. *"And if he sins against you seven times in a day, and seven times in a day returns to you, saying, 'I repent,' you shall forgive him."*
    -   **Luke 17:4 (NKJV)**

FAMOUS QUOTES:

1. *"When we think we have been hurt by someone in the past, we build up defenses to protect ourselves from being hurt in the future. So, the fearful past causes a fearful future and the past and future become one. We cannot love when we feel fear... When we release the fearful past and forgive everyone, we will experience total love and oneness with all."*
   - **Gerald G. Jampolsky**

2. *"Resentment is like drinking poison and then hoping it will kill your enemies."*
   - **Nelson Mandela**

3. *"A heart filled with anger has no room for love."*
   - **Joan Lunden**

TAKEAWAYS:

1. Counselors vs. Coaching: Counselors and psychologist normally help you deal with emotional pains of the past, while life coaches help you design the future of your dreams. Some people actually have both, a counselor and a life coach.

2. If you are in an emotional hole at fourteen-years-old, you will still be in that hole at 64-years-old if no one ever teaches you how to CLIMB.

3. *CLIMB*ing means you have to take ACTION to change your life.

4. It is sad when someone says, "I've survived this long without any help, so I will continue to survive without it." Unfortunately, surviving is not a way to live in victory. We want to be open to change so that we can live an amazing life.

AFFIRMATIONS: *(Recite each morning)*

1. I will seek wise counsel weekly to keep my mind sharp.
2. I will read one book a week on the same subject matter to become an expert in two years.

TIME TO CLIMB:

Exercise 1: FIND A MENTOR, COUNSELOR, SPIRITUAL COUNSELOR, OR LIFE COACH

Materials needed: Phone

Places to find mentors: School staff, church, community centers, police department, fire departments, fraternities, sororities, co-workers of parents, friends of parents, uncles, aunts, etc.

1. Call your parents or guardians and ask them if they could recommend a good mentor, counselor, or life coach.

2. Give them ideas from the list above.

3. Call the person that they recommend or call someone who you want to be your mentor.

4. Once someone agrees to be your mentor, it is your responsibility to make contact with that person.

5. Schedule at least 4 bi-weekly meetings with them immediately. Try to schedule for the same day of the week at the same time, for example every other Friday at noon.

6. If you meet at breakfast, lunch, or dinner, be sure to pay for their food. Never expect your mentor to buy your meal. Note: No matter how famous, rich, or important a person may be, everyone loves a FREE LUNCH.

Exercise 2: MEETING WITH YOUR MENTOR, COUNSELOR, SPIRITUAL COUNSELOR OR LIFE COACH

Materials needed: Calendar, notebook, pen, and short and long-term goals

1. Always be prepared when meeting with your mentor.

2. Show your mentor your goals and ask them for the best way to achieve those goals. They may have the knowledge or connections to help you achieve your goals faster.

3. Pay for their lunch, thank them for their time, and schedule the next meetings before departing.

Chapter 7

SPIRITUALITY

"You don't have to believe what I believe but believe in something outside of yourself."

- Roderick Cunningham

If we are to have a healthy mind, body, and spirit, we have to speak about spirituality. Spirituality is a very broad concept and includes a sense of connection to something bigger than ourselves. If you ask fifty people to define spirituality, you will get fifty different answers. Spirituality and religion are two different, but complimentary concepts.

Spirituality:

- Where do I find meaning for my life?
- How do I feel connected to people, places, or things?
- How should I live my life?

Religion:

- What rituals should I follow?
- What is right and what is wrong?
- What is true and what is false?

Religions and religious organizations have developed systems, practices, and rituals to answer your questions on spirituality. Now, you must decide which religion gives you comfort and aligns with your beliefs and ethics.

My personal belief is that we have three different spirits that dwell within us.

- The evil spirit that we call the devil or darkness
- The holy spirit that we call the angel or light
- The human spirit that makes you do things that feel good to you

Whichever spirit you feed the most, will be the spirit that comes out through your actions. For example:

1. If you listen to explicit (laced in profanity) rap or rock music, which spirit are you feeding?
2. If you look at pornographic images, which spirit are you feeding?

3. If you feed the homeless, which spirit are you feeding?
4. If you listen to Gospel music that stirs your spirit, which spirit are you feeding?
5. If you read the Bible, which spirit are you feeding?

One of the three spirits will guide your life if you don't take control of your own life. If your spirit instructs you to "punch him in the face," and you do just that, then you are most likely being guided by a dark spirit that we call the devil.

Your spirit is modified by what comes into your senses of touch, smell, taste, hearing, and seeing. We call these "gates" and you have to "GUARD YOUR GATES."

If you want to be guided by the light or the holy spirit, then you should study the book to learn the systems, practices, and rituals of your chosen religion, pray, meditate, and listen to spiritual music that connects with your soul. If you do this often, you will have less of the devil speaking softly in your head, and more of the holy spirit speaking softly in your head and guiding your life to success, happiness, and victory.

Have you ever met anyone that made your skin crawl? You may have said to yourself, "Oooh, I don't like his spirit at all."

Have you watched your new boyfriend/girlfriend enter a room and/or give you a certain kind of eye contact and you get butterflies in your stomach? That means that your spirits are connected. It means that you are on the same vibration or frequency. We all operate on different frequencies, but when we meet someone on our same frequency, there is an instant connection and both people can feel it. We say things like, "Our spirits just gelled immediately."

Have you ever heard someone sing and it gave you goosebumps? That means that you are on the same frequency and in total vibration with the singer. Everyone won't feel the same way. That's why we have so many genres of music. Additionally, we many different kinds of cars on the road. Everyone likes what connects with them, based on their frequency.

TAMMY

"You think I need you Tom? Well I don't! All you do is get drunk and flirt with women!" Tammy's mother was yelling at the top of her lungs at her father.

"Maybe if you would check your attitude I would be home more Shelby!" Thomas yelled back on his way out of the door, slamming it as he left.

Tammy stood at her window crying while she watched her father speed away in his car. She wished she could go with him and she felt upset with her mother because in her five-year-old mind, it was her fault that he left. Her parents had been arguing a lot and it caused Thomas to stay away from home more than he usually did. Tammy was a major daddy's girl and it hurt her to not see him as much as she was accustomed to. When things were good with her parents, Tammy spent all of her time with her father, he took her to get ice cream, to the beach, and sometimes he even played with her dolls with her just to see her smile.

After a year of arguing on almost a daily basis, Tammy's parents finally got divorced. Thomas pulled Tammy aside one day and said to her, "Look baby girl, Mommy and Daddy are not going to live together anymore. You and I are not going to see each other every day like we do now, but I want you to know that I still love you. Never forget that you are my baby and you mean the world to me."

Tammy had heard her mother talking to her friend Sasha, and using the word "divorce," but until this moment, she didn't know what it meant.

"Well. can I just come with you daddy? I want to live with you," said Tammy as tears rolled down her cheeks.

Tammy clung to her father as she begged, but eventually he was able to calm her down with a promise that she could come visit him every weekend.

At first, things were actually better for Tammy after her parents' divorce. She didn't have to hear any arguing, and when she visited her father he gave her all of his attention. What she didn't know was that her mother was struggling to pay bills and they would eventually have to move in with her uncle and their three children. Tammy was the only girl living in the household, and she longed for the weekends to get away from her annoying cousins.

She loved going to her father's apartment. He had two bedrooms, so she had her own space. On one particular Friday, Tammy was packed and ready for her dad to pick her up when she received a call from him.

"Hey baby girl, I'm on the way to pick you up and I have a surprise for you!"

"Ooh what kind of surprise daddy? Is it a puppy? Please tell me it's a puppy." Tammy was beaming from ear to ear, unable to hold in her excitement.

When she hung up the phone she rushed to get her things together and waited on the porch for her father to pull up.

"Why are you so happy Tammy?" Tammy's cousin, Rick, came on the porch from the yard, intrigued by her huge smile.

"My daddy is coming to get me, and he said he's got a surprise for me." She spoke proudly and was glad that her cousins would see her special surprise when her father arrived.

After a few moments, Thomas pulled up and Tammy strained to see into the car. She was confused when she noticed someone riding in the front seat with him. She wondered who the person was and why they were there.

Thomas hopped out of his car with a smile and said, "Hey baby girl!" He stood there with his arms open waiting for Tammy to rush into them like she usually does.

Tammy yelled, "Daddy, daddy," as she ran into his arms.

After a big bear hug from her father, Tammy was anxious to see what her surprise was.

"Well sweetheart, I have someone with me who really wants to meet you." Thomas motioned for his passenger to get out of the car.

A beautiful woman stepped out of the car and smiled in Tammy's direction. She was tall, with flawless brown skin and a perfect smile, and she clutched onto a small bag.

"This is daddy's friend Gisselle," said Thomas. Tammy looked up at the woman and gave her a quiet hello while eyeing the bag that she was clutching.

"Hello Tammy, well aren't you gorgeous? This is for you," said Gisselle as she smiled and offered the bag to Tammy.

"Okay you two, let's hit the road, I'm starving." Thomas said while putting Tammy's things in the trunk.

Over the course of the day Tammy started to warm up to Gisselle a little bit. She was so nice that it was hard not to like her. She owned a spa and took Tammy there to get her nails and toes done and it made Tammy feel so grown up. Although she had a great time, she was happy when her father dropped Gisselle off. She missed having all of his attention.

As time passed, Tammy saw Gisselle more and more, and eventually Gisselle moved into her father's apartment. By the time Tammy turned ten-years-old, her father had married Gisselle. Tammy's mother also eventually married her boyfriend Kevin, and they were finally able to move out of her uncle's house.

Soon after her father and Gisselle married, her little brother, Payton, was born. Before she knew it, her room at her father's apartment had been turned into a nursery. Thomas promised that she would not have to sleep in his living room when she visited forever, it was only until their new home was built, where Tammy would have her own room again. Tammy's mother had also given birth to her little sister Shanice that year. Eventually it got to the point that Tammy was only visiting her father once a month. Thomas was always busy with Payton or working overtime. Tammy started to get frustrated with hearing her father's excuses, and eventually stopped calling him for months at a time.

Time passed, and neither of her parents seemed to notice how much Tammy was hurting. One day, when she was fourteen-years-old, Tammy got into an argument with her mother. She wanted to go to the movies with some friends and asked her mom for $20.00. Her mom said that she was sorry, but she did not have it at the time.

"Ugh! So, you can buy Shanice every toy in the store, but I can't get $20.00 to see a movie? That's BS!" Yelled Tammy as she slammed down the bowl of spaghetti that she had been heating in the microwave.

Shelby was shocked that Tammy had spoken to her in that way and before she could say anything, Kevin stepped in.

"No ma'am young lady! You will not speak to your mother that way while you are living under our roof!" He folded his arms and gave her a stern look, although he spoke calmly.

"You're not my daddy! Nobody cares about me. Now that everyone has toddlers in the house, I'm nothing!" She stormed off into her room wiping a tear from her eye as she walked away.

That incident seemed to be the turning point in Tammy's adolescence. She started to stay in her room more and more. She would even wait until the rest of the family had eaten dinner, and then take hers and eat it in her room. Throughout her middle school years, she was a straight A student, but as she entered high school, her grades started to slip. When she was home, she spent almost all her time in her room talking to friends and using social media.

Tammy was incredibly smart and did well in school with little effort. She graduated on time with a 3.5 GPA. If she would have given school all her effort, she could have easily been valedictorian. She decided that it would be best for her to get out of Miami for college, so she opted for a school in Atlanta. Tammy enjoyed the change of scenery and within three months of college, she met Boris... his friends called him Bo. He quite literally ran into her one day while she was on her way to class. He was tall, with a caramel complexion, and he had a lot of tattoos. She was immediately attracted to him and they began dating soon after they met.

The thing that Tammy liked the most about Boris was that he was mysterious. One day they were at his place relaxing and Boris took his shirt off. Tammy noticed that among all his other tattoos, he had a huge portrait of someone tattooed on his chest.

She sat on his lap to get a closer look and asked who it was. At that moment, for the first time, she saw Bo's vulnerable side.

 "That's my brother. He died when he was eighteen and I was sixteen." Bo had a blank look on his face, he stared at the floor as he spoke.

Tammy searched for the words to comfort Bo, but when she couldn't find them, she grabbed his neck and kissed him on the forehead. That seemed to do the job, she could feel him relax, and for the first time, he opened up to her about his childhood. He told Tammy about his father and how harsh he was, and how his mother closed herself off for years after his brother's passing. She felt bad that Bo had to go through such a rough time as a teenager and promised him that she would always be there for him. A few weeks later, Bo told Tammy that he loved her, and she instantly fell head-over-heels for him. No boy had ever told Tammy that he loved her, and she was convinced that Bo was her soulmate.

Tammy was a very social person in college, so even though she had only been there for a short time, she had a lot of friends, none of whom liked Bo. They thought that she could do much better with one of the full-time students, maybe one in a fraternity. They only saw Bo from the outside, they saw him come to class with stains on his clothes, and Tammy saw a kid who worked full-time to support himself and squeezed college in to chase his dreams. They saw a guy with un-kept hair and a body covered in tattoos, while Tammy saw a free spirit who wore dreadlocks and tattoos as a form of expression. They didn't like how Bo spoke to Tammy at times because he could become very short and snappy with his words, but in her mind, they didn't understand him. He was only short tempered because of what he had been through.

One weekend, Tammy's mom and Shanice came to visit her. Tammy was nervous because this was the first time that her mother was going to meet Bo. Bo saved up money to rent a car, and got his roommate who was older, to put it in his name. Bo and Tammy drove to the airport to pick up Shelby and Shanice and they all went to dinner afterwards. Tammy didn't want her mother to know that she had basically moved out of her dorm room, so instead of going back to Bo's apartment, she asked him to drop her, her mother and sister back off to the dorms.

When they got back into the dorm room Tammy asked her mother what she thought about Bo.

"Well baby, I don't know if Bo is right for you. I noticed at dinner that he interrupted you as you were speaking, and he didn't even give you a chance to order your own food. College is a unique time in your life Tam. You have the freedom to find yourself while you're gaining your education. Once college is over, you will have all the time in the world to date, but for now I want you to focus on yourself. The last thing you want is to get pregnant by a guy who isn't ready to be a father and isn't equipped to take care of a baby."

Tammy was annoyed by her mother's response and hoped for once that she would just support her.

"Whoa mom, who is talking about getting pregnant and having babies? I really love Boris and I don't deny that he has flaws, but so do I. He makes me feel good about myself and I am smart enough to know that he loves me."

Shelby did not want any tension between herself and Tammy, so she backed down and said, "Okay sweetheart, you just have to understand that I am your mother and it is my job to protect you, and to protect your heart if I need to. Just be careful."

They talked a little while longer and eventually Shelby and Shanice went to check into their hotel. Tammy tried to call Bo once they left, but he wasn't answering. She figured he must have gone out with his roommate Chris. He didn't end up calling her until the next morning and Tammy was a little upset. She asked him to please at least send her a text when he's out, so she would know that he was okay. Bo promised that it wouldn't happen again, and all was well.

Six months later, Tammy completely moved out of her dorm room and into Bo's apartment. One night, Bo and Chris went out again, but before he left, Bo told Tammy that he would be back around midnight. Midnight passed, and then 1:00 AM and then 2:00 AM. Tammy must have called Bo fifty times that night with no answer. At 5:00 AM Bo came stumbling into their room and he was very drunk. Tammy could not hold in her anger. She yelled at Bo for about thirty minutes straight. She called him stupid and told him that he needed to step-up and be a real man. Once she was done yelling, she looked over at Bo as he was looking at her the same way that her father used to look at her mother after she yelled at him. After a moment of silence, she pulled Bo close to her and kissed his forehead.

"I'm sorry for yelling babe, please don't be mad at me. I just wanted to make sure that you were okay. I love you."

At that moment, Bo realized that he could do what he wanted, and Tammy wouldn't leave him, so the pattern continued. He went out with his friends, and Tammy waited up for him. She yelled at him for a few minutes and then apologized afterwards. Bo would actually brag to his friends that he controlled the relationship with Tammy because she has "daddy issues."

Two years into their relationship, Tammy gave birth to their daughter Beatrice. Tammy couldn't have been more in love with their daughter. For the first time since she was a little girl, she felt unconditional love. It wasn't from her father, or her boyfriend, it was from her baby girl, and for that reason, Tammy started focusing on getting her life on track for Bebe.

She stopped waiting up for Bo at night. Instead of him coming home to Tammy yelling at him, she and Bebe would be sound asleep. One Saturday morning, Tammy woke Bo up, who had come home drunk just a few hours earlier, and told him that she was moving back to Miami with Bebe. Tammy knew that Bo loved Bebe, but she had to get her daughter into a more stable environment. Bob egged Tammy not to leave and promised that he would change for them. Tammy was tired of giving Bo chances and being disappointed by broken promises. She told Botha she wasn't leaving to hurt him, she was leaving to make a better life for their daughter. She grabbed the back of his neck and kissed his forehead one last time and she left. She felt a sense of guilt for leaving Bo behind and cried the whole way to the airport.

Kevin and Shelby were waiting for Tammy when she landed back home in Miami. She saw them from a distance when she headed towards the door and thought about how she felt as a teenager. She vowed to herself that she would make sure that Bebe never felt the pain that she did. She would give her everything, and she convinced herself that Bebe didn't need Bo. For the first year after she left, Bo would call her while he was drunk and beg her to come back, then he would use heavy doses of profanity when she denied his requests. She eventually got to the point that she only answered his calls on Bebe's birthday and on holidays.

At age twenty-two, Tammy gave her life to Christ and became a Christian. She learned to trust in Him and started to live her life in a way that she felt was pleasing to Him. She started reading her bible daily, meditating on the words that she was reading, praying for change in her life, and volunteering at her church. After a few years of living with her mother, Tammy saved enough money to buy a car and to get her own place. She was doing well, and she remained single. She had finally taken her mother's advice and was focused on bettering herself. One evening after Bible study, one of the guys from the church approached Tammy. He was tall, sported a short and neat haircut, and dressed very nicely. As he approached Tammy, he extended his hand.

"Good evening, I'm Romeo. How are you?"

Tammy shook Romeo's hand and introduced herself. They chatted for a while and Tammy eventually agreed to go out for coffee with him the next morning. The two took things slowly but after six months, they found themselves head-over-heels in love. Tammy knew that Romeo was different, he was a devout Christian, and they encouraged each other to live the best lives that they could. Romeo also treated Bebe as if she was his own. He loved her and spent time with her. Tammy was convinced that with Romeo as a father figure, Bebe would be just fine without Bo. Eighteen months into their relationship, Romeo proposed, and they were married a year later.

Tammy felt that her family was finally complete except for one detail. Bo still struggled with his sobriety and depression, so Tammy figured that Bebe would be better off if Romeo was able to adopt her. She figured Bo would be happy to be done with any responsibilities other than himself. She decided to call him and ask for him to sign over his rights. The conversation could not have gone any worse. Bo completely exploded. Tammy had never heard Bo speak that harshly to her, he was so out of control that she had to end the call but not before she did a little exploding of her own. She told Bo that Bebe had a new dad and she didn't need him in her life anymore. Had she been there, she would have seen that Bo was so angry that he threw his cell phone across the room and shattered it. He cried and cried for over an hour. After that Tammy didn't answer any more of Bo's calls.

One year into their marriage, Tammy and Romeo welcomed their daughter Andrea and four years later, their son Romeo Jr. When Bebe was fourteen, her eight-year-old little sister Andrea asked, "Bebe, where's your daddy? We never see him but you're always with our daddy."

Andrea never meant any harm by her question, but it started a sense of division in Bebe's mind even though she and Romeo always had a great relationship. Over the next few weeks, Bebe started to isolate herself from the rest of the family. She would say that no one cared about her, that they were only worried about Romeo Jr. and Andrea. Tammy tried to assure Bebe that nothing could be further from the truth, but no matter how much one-on-one time she spent with her or how much love she gave her, Bebe was still unhappy.

One night, Tammy was relaxing with a glass of wine and checking her messages on social media. She saw a message from Boris Jackson and almost deleted it. She hadn't heard anything from him in years and figured he was the same old Bo trying to come in and cause chaos. Just as she was about to delete the message, she had a flashback to her childhood. She thought about how she longed for a relationship with her biological father and wondered what kind of mother she would be if she took that option off the table for Bebe. She decided to read Bo's message and from what she read it seemed that he was a changed man. He said he had stopped drinking and got counseling for his depression. He said that he was trying to be a better man, and the first step was to apologize to his daughter.

The message seemed vulnerable and honest, it reminded her of the night that he told her about his brother's death. Tammy decided that she would ask Bebe how she felt about it. She went up to Bebe's room and saw a new "Do Not Disturb" sign on her door. She stood there for a moment and knew what she had to do.

"Bebe, can I come in?" Tammy tapped on the door as she spoke.

"Sure, I guess." Bebe called back.

Tammy sat on Bebe's bed and explained that her father reached out and wanted to talk to her. She explained that Bo had a really hard life and wanted to start to make things right. She asked if Bebe wanted her to give Bo her phone number and Bebe flashed a smile that Tammy hadn't seen in months. With tears in her eyes, Bebe responded, "Please mom, I want to know my dad."

That phone call between Bebe and Bo was magical, and they began to talk every day. Their relationship began to grow, and they began spending time together.

NOTE: Bebe did not have her father in her life at the age of fourteen. Tammy did not have her father in her life at the age of fourteen. Tammy's mother did not have her father in her life at the age of fourteen. Tammy's grandmother did not have her father in her life at the age of fourteen etc. How far back can this kind of generational curse go? Unfortunately, it could be hundreds of years. If Tammy is African-American, it could reach as far back as slavery. Do we have any documentation that slaves were given emotional counseling for childhood trauma that put them in an emotional hole? The trauma may have come from slave owners who sold the fathers away from their wives and children. Children often watched their brothers, fathers and uncles get degraded, beaten, shot, sold away from their family, and/or hung, while their mothers and other female family members get raped and/or beaten. Is it possible that if that kind of trauma happened hundreds of years ago, without counseling, then those generational curses can still be in existence for another hundred years if we don't do something about it? Whatever happens in our family as children, quickly becomes NORMAL to us. We only question our NORMS if we are constantly exposed to right behavior. We have got to do what we can to stop the generational curse and begin to seek counseling as well as the four other ways of climbing out of the emotional hole.

QUESTIONS:

1. Do you think that Romeo's biological children will fall into a similar emotional hole as Bebe?   Why or why not?

2. Do you think that Romeo can be the greatest step-dad in the world, yet Bebe can still be in an emotional hole?
   YES | NO | MAYBE

3. After Bebe's little sister makes the statement about Bebe's biological father, do you think Bebe began to think of Bo more often, where she consciously or sub-consciously began to yearn for a better relationship with her biological father?
   YES | NO | MAYBE

4. Do you think that a simple comment from an eight-year-old could change the way Bebe feels about her relationship with Tammy, Romeo, and Bo?
   YES | NO | MAYBE

5. Can the Five Ways to Conquer Your Life (Table 3-1) help Tammy, Bo, and/or Bebe?

a. Who does Bebe need to be **FORGIVE**?

b. Who does Tammy need to **FORGIVE**?

c. Who needs COUNSELING?   TAMMY | BO | BEBE | ALL 3

d. Who can benefit from finding PURPOSE in their life?
TAMMY | BO | BEBE | ALL 3

e. Who could benefit from WRITING in a daily journal?
TAMMY | BO | BEBE | ALL 3

f. Who could benefit from SPIRITUAL development?
TAMMY | BO | BEBE | ALL 3

6. Do you think if Tammy had listened to her friends and her mom's advice to ignore Bo, finish college, and then meet Romeo, that her life could have been much easier?

Note: The purpose here is not to look at Bebe as a mistake, but to help young ladies in real life to make sound decisions about relationships *prior* to meeting someone like Bo.

7. Do you think that Bo would have married Tammy if she would have said, "No sex and no babies before marriage?"
YES | NO | MAYBE

8. Do you think Tammy would have chosen Bo if she and her father had daily conversations and if he was giving her sound advice about dating in college and the importance of finishing college?
YES | NO | MAYBE

SPIRITUAL REFERENCES:

1. *"When they bring you, betrayed, into court, don't worry about what you'll say. When the time comes, say what's on your heart—the Holy Spirit will make his witness in and through you."*
   - **Mark 13:11 (MSG)**

2. *"He'll drink neither wine nor beer. He'll be filled with the Holy Spirit from the moment he leaves his mother's womb."*
   - **Luke 1:15 (MSG)**

FAMOUS QUOTES:

1. *"The essential lesson I've learned in life is to just be yourself. Treasure the magnificent being that you are and recognize first and foremost you're not here as a human being only. You're a spiritual being having a human experience."*
   - **Wayne Dyer**

2. *"It is through gratitude for the present moment that the spiritual dimension of life opens up."*
   - **Eckhart Tolle**

3. *"The world sometimes feels like an insane asylum. You can decide whether you want to be an inmate or pick up your visitor's badge. You can be in the world but not engage in the melodrama of it; you can become a spiritual being having a human experience thoroughly and fully. Deepak Chopra."*
   - **Deepak Chopra**

TAKEAWAYS:

1. **Young ladies**: Be patient because Romeo is coming and listen to your family when they tell you that Bo is not good for you. Your family is not challenging your decision to pick your own mate, but they can see things that you may be blind to because you are emotionally attached to the person. They are using intelligence and rational thinking while looking at the whole picture. You can't see the picture when you are in the frame. Is it possible for your parents and friends to be wrong about Bo? Sure, that possibility exists; no one is right 100% of the time.

I would challenge you to look at Bo's norms, meaning his normal behavior based on how he was raised and what he was taught by his parents, siblings, uncles, etc. about what life and relationships are all about. You can't ignore how a person acts under pressure. Because when most people are under pressure, they run to their vices for comfort. Here are a few things to consider right away before you become emotionally attached to a Bo:

- What is his relationship with his biological parents?

- How did he grow up?

- Who is teaching him what manhood is all about?

- What is his chosen vice when he is stressed with life, career, finances, or relationships? Does he smoke, do drugs, drink, gamble, fight, retreat (shutdown), read, play video games all night, go to the club, flirt with other women, watch pornography, have sex, drag race, watch football, etc.

- Who is his mentor and/or his role models?

- Who makes up his Four Personal Pillars of Trust?

- How deep is his emotional hole?

- If he already has children, how much time does he spend with them?

Unfortunately, good girls like bad boys when daddy is not an active part of their lives. These good girls want to change their Bo and mold him into the man *they* want him to be. Remember, men don't just wake up one day and decide to change who they are just because a woman yells and screams at him. If any man stays in a relationship filled with yelling and screaming, he will just shut down, go deeper into his emotional hole, and begin focusing more on his vices. If Bo is willing to change, this book will help him out of his emotional hole and help him to grow into the man that he was destined to be. Give Bo the tools to mature into that man, but **don't have babies** with him until that maturity manifests change in his life and he "puts a ring on it" and you guys get married.

You have to teach men how to treat you and if you don't know how you want to be treated, then how will he know. I have heard women say, "He should know how to treat me. I don't think I need to raise a man; his mother should have done that." You have to teach a man how to talk to you with respect, how to hold you when you want to be held, what time respectable people come home from being out with friends, how to recognize your non-verbal signs when you are ready to leave a public outing, how to communicate with and respect your parents/siblings/friends, and how to respond to other females when not in your presence, etc.

Men are knuckleheads by nature and we normally say stupid things, do stupid things, and stupid ideas come into our brains constantly. We simply need love, support, patience, and understanding from our family. We need mentorship/ counseling/coaching from successful people, we need to forgive, we need to develop a spiritual life, and we need to set real goals for our future and the future success of our family.

2. **Young men**: Don't be a Bo. Treat women with love and respect. Don't get a girl pregnant so that you can feel like more of a man. Don't allow your emotional pain to stop a young lady from completing her dream of finishing college and getting married to someone who truly loves her. Become teachable and coachable and don't feel as though you have life all figured out. Be sure to read the section above for Young Ladies at least three times. Find yourself a mature mentor as fast as possible. It is your responsibility to reach out to your mentor at least once per week. If you don't call him when you need to talk, how will he know that you are in need?

Women were designed to be sweet, loving, and to believe that what we say is truth. We can't take advantage of this love because it will only alter the way that she loves others in the future. As men, we should always want our current or our ex-girlfriend/ex-wife to be successful in love. If we are no longer in a relationship with them, we don't want to stop them from loving someone else because love is healthy for our hearts, mind, spirit, and body. If you never intend to love that women again romantically, then release her (tell her how you truly feel... tell her that the love you feel is philia love "brotherly/sisterly" love) so that she can move on and find her Romeo who will show her romantic love called Eros love.

3. **Mothers**: Be careful sending your girls to college unprepared for men like Bo (consider having a forum of men talking with your daughter before she leaves for college/military). Just give the mentors this book and show them Tammy's story. They will know what to say to your daughter. Remember, your children want love and

acceptance from their mother and father. They never tire of hearing, "I am so proud of you." I make it a point to reach out to my adult children at least once per week to let them know that I am proud of them and that I love them. They have never asked me to stop saying it.

Although you recognize that your children may or may not be well prepared for what life will throw at them, you have to allow life to give them those lessons. Your job is to be there to catch them when they fall. Don't allow your children to go more than three days without talking to you while they are away from you. If there are disagreements between you two, fix them now. You may not have time to fix them later because tomorrow is not promised. I attended a funeral yesterday for a twenty-four-year-old Army Sergeant who lost his life in a kayaking accident at his Army Post. I wonder if he and his mother and father were talking two to three times per week? Or if one of them said, my son is tripping right now, when he wakes up from the foolishness, he will call me, and we can talk. What if that wake-up call never comes? Are you prepared to live with that emotional pain?

4. **Fathers**: Call your sons and daughters at least three times per week while they are in college. They need you more when they leave home because they will have to make some major decisions they never had to make before. They may act as though they don't need you or want you around, but trust me, they do. Also, drop by the campus once per month to check on your son/daughter and meet their friends. Be prepared to take some long walks with boys/young men to explain the rules of dating your daughter. When a young man knows that a girl has a father, uncle, or grandfather in her corner that is willing to look him eye ball to eye ball, that young man will leave the girl alone if he does not have good intentions for her. Additionally, it is very important to "respect" the mother of your children, whether you are still together or not. I will venture to say that 80% of the women in an emotional hole are there because of a man.

5. **Families**: It is time to break the generational curse. It is important for men to stay at home with their wives and raise their children. Many times, marital relationships can survive if both parents decide to get counseling, especially counseling that deals with anger, sadness, guilt, fear, and hurt. Do not be afraid to get counseling and ask for help. Since many marital relationships break up due to infidelity (cheating), and since cheating and sexual immorality comes from being in an emotional hole, then counseling, finding purpose, forgiveness, journaling, and spiritual development can

help keep the family together. In other words, when you climb out of your emotional hole, you minimize your stress, which minimizes your need to depend on your vices for comfort.

AFFIRMATIONS: *(Recite each morning)*

1. I will guard my spiritual gate at all times and allow mostly positivity in my space.
2. I will read my religious guide at least ten minutes each day so that I can understand the spiritual expectations of my religion.

TIME TO CLIMB:

Exercise 1: PRAY, READ, AND MEDITATE ON WHAT YOU READ

Materials needed: Smartphone with a Bible App or App with your religious book

Time: 5-7 minutes

1. Close your eyes and ask God for strength, forgiveness, purpose, and clarity for your life.
2. Read two verses of Proverbs
3. Sit quietly and figure out what it means and how can you apply it in your life.

"Vision without execution is hallucination"

- Thomas Edison

Chapter 8

PURPOSE

"The two most important days in your life are the day you are born and the day you find out why".

- Mark Twain

Purpose = PERSONAL Power

PERSONAL Power + Purpose = Provision

Provision = Financial Stability

After reaching middle age and discovering that life is too short to squander it chasing money, buying fancy things, and not living a life of purpose, many people in their 40s began to search for their life's purpose.

Young millennials today are more in-tuned with their emotions and are searching for their purpose as early as fifteen-years-old. In this age of social media, young people are able to see the ills of our society every day by picking up their cell phones and logging into their social media sites. This has driven them to want to become a part of the solution and not the problem. Young people are discovering early that they have a voice to affect change, whether it's the #MeToo movement (sexual harassment), #BlackLivesMatter movement (police shootings of unarmed African-Americans), or the #MarchForOurLives movement (school shooting survivors from Parkland, FL enacting gun control laws in the state and nationally).

Additionally, there are many reality television shows that will capture their attention and help them discover who and what they want to be. There are reality shows that highlight gardening, cooking, fishing, entrepreneurship, real estate, community advocacy, philanthropy, etc.

Purpose involves what you do for other people. Purpose has nothing to do with you, it is about the value you create in the lives of others. How is someone else's life better because you lived?

TANISHA

"Hello? Earth to Tanisha!" Jasmine said while waiving her hand in front of her best friend's face. Tanisha was forced out of her day dream by the sound of Jasmine's voice. "Hey Jas, sorry I was in my own world over here." Tanisha replied with a toothy grin.
"So, I see. Tanisha, now that we're seniors, we have to make sure that all of the slots for FPL are filled before the end of the semester," said Jasmine.

Tanisha and Jasmine were leaders of a group in their school called Faith, Purity, and Love. The group consisted of students that had taken a vow of celibacy until marriage.

Tanisha had always been popular among her peers, she was beautiful, smart, and down to earth. Above all those qualities, the one that stood out most was the fact that she was able to unapologetically be herself. She somehow seemed to be immune to the pressures of being a teenager and was always able to stick to her morals while never coming off as judgmental towards others.

As Tanisha and Jasmine continued their conversation about FPL they noticed some commotion coming from the other end of the hallway. Troy the Viking, the school mascot, was leading the football team through the hallway getting the students excited for the first game of the season.

He danced his way toward Tanisha and Jasmine yelling, "Go Vikings!"

As he approached the girls, they returned his cheers and high-fived the players as they passed.

"We're hitting the game tonight with the girls, right?" Jasmine asked Tanisha.

"The first game! Of course, what kind of Viking would I be if I missed it?" Tanisha replied with a laugh.

Jasmine and Tanisha were also close friends with Trish and Veronica. Although all four girls had grown up together, Trish and Veronica had become somewhat opposite of Tanisha and Jasmine. Trish and Veronica had sexual experiences with boys and they gently teased Tanisha and Jasmine about their vow of celibacy.

That afternoon the four girls went shopping to find the perfect outfits. They were playing against their rival team and they knew the game would be packed. After their shopping trip, they went to Veronica's house to hang out until it was time for the game.

When the girls arrived at the game, they could hear the music from the band battling the cheers from the crowd. The concession stands filled the air with the savory aroma of hot dogs and burgers from the grill.

The girls commanded attention as they navigated through the crowd. They were all known for being well-dressed and they unknowingly set the standard for what was cool in high school. They waived to familiar faces in the crowd as they heard their names ring out among the cheers. They sat near the 50-yard line and cheered on their team. The game was an intense battle between two very good teams. The Vikings led 34 to 30. With 90 seconds remaining in the 4th quarter, the visiting Dragons' cornerback stripped the ball out of the hands of the school's star running back. The Dragons recovered the fumble with 75 seconds left. After a tough defensive stand by the Vikings, it was 4th and 7, the ball was on the 50-yard-line, and there were ten seconds left in the game. The Dragons' quarterback dropped back, scrambled with the ball, and threw a hail Mary pass into the end zone. The Dragon's receiver caught the ball in the end zone to win the game.

After the game Tanisha and the girls headed back to the car and made plans for the rest of the night. They had to pass the Dragons' players on the way back to their car. The quarterback locked eyes with Tanisha and flashed a toothy grin. Although she was taken back by his hazel eyes and perfect smile, she simply gave him a partial smile and kept talking with her friends. Trish noticed the whole encounter and couldn't resist calling Tanisha out on it.

"Uh oh, it looks like somebody's got a fan." She said through a laugh while nudging Tanisha.

"Is he still looking?" Tanisha asks. "Yes girl, and if you don't get his number I promise I will," Veronica said, as she and Trish laughed and high-fived each other.

"Tanisha, he's coming over here," Jasmine said with a smile.

By the time Tanisha turned around he was only a few feet away.

"Hey ladies, what's up? I'm Ray," he said to all of them while keeping his eyes on Tanisha.

"Ugh, those eyes and that smile again," Tanisha thought to herself.

"Tough break on that fumble," he said jokingly.

They all laughed, and Tanisha introduced herself and the girls. After a brief conversation, Ray asked Tanisha for her phone number, and although she was attracted to him, she was reluctant to give it to him for some reason that she couldn't pinpoint. Eventually, she decided that it wasn't a big deal and put her number into his phone.

At the time, Tanisha acted as if she wasn't that impressed by Ray, but on the days following, she found herself checking her phone more than usual, looking for a call or text from an unfamiliar number.

The call finally came on Tuesday of the next week. Ray called Tanisha at around 6:00 PM and they talked well past midnight. They got to know each other, they talked about school, their families, and their dreams for the future. Tanisha found out that Ray was the top quarterback in the state and had plans on attending Florida State University before entering the professional football draft. He also shared with her that his father passed away when he was five-years old and his mother had never remarried. Tanisha shared her dream of attending Spellman University and becoming a teacher. By the end of the call they had already planned their first date for the upcoming Saturday. As they said goodnight Tanisha heard a light knocking at her door.

"It's open, come in," Tanisha said while stuffing her phone under her blanket.

Her father cracked the door and poked his head in and said, "Baby girl, it's kind of late, you should probably get some sleep for school tomorrow. I don't want you to be late."

"OK daddy, I'm headed to sleep right now," she replied.

"Ok baby girl, good night. I love you," said her father.

"Love you too daddy," she replied.

As her father disappeared from her doorway, Tanisha replayed her and Ray's conversation in her head. She felt a tinge of sadness for Ray when she imagined what it must have been like to grow up without his dad. She drifted off into a deep sleep feeling excited about their upcoming date.

After what seemed like a lifetime, Saturday finally arrived. Tanisha spent the better part of her day preparing for her big date with Ray. At about 7:00 PM Ray arrived at Tanisha's house. He had a certain charm to his personality and he knew it, so he never had any issues with meeting the parents of any girl that he dated. He got out of his car, walked to the front door with confidence, and rang the bell. Tanisha's mother answered.

"Good evening Ma'am, I'm Raymond Donovan. You must be Mrs. Williams," Ray said as he extended his hand and flashed that perfect smile.

Before Mrs. Williams could shake Ray's hand, Mr. Williams appeared and shook Ray's hand with an intentionally extra firm grip. After Mrs. Williams cut her eyes at her husband as to say, "Would you calm down," she said to Ray, "Come in Raymond, Tanisha has told us all about you. Have a seat sweetheart, she should be down in a moment."

Tanisha could hear both her father's and Ray's voices from her bathroom and decided that she had better get downstairs before Ray changed his mind about wanting to date her. As she made her way down the stairs she eyed Ray before he had a chance to notice her. He looked like he had just left the barbershop and he was dressed nicely. He wore a nice pair of white sneakers, jeans that actually fit, a button up shirt, and his letterman jacket.

"You just had to wear the Dragons jacket huh?" Tanisha called out as she entered the foyer.

Ray laughed, partly at Tanisha's joke, and partly to escape the interrogation that he was getting from her father. Tanisha saved him from "the talk" by ensuring her father that they would drive safely and return home at a decent hour.

As they left the house Ray complimented Tanisha's outfit and jokingly called her a hater for commenting on his school's jacket. She assured him that his winning touchdown pass was a fluke and that it wouldn't happen again. They laughed and joked all the way to the movie theater. Although Ray had dated plenty of girls from his school, none of them were as smart, classy, or beautiful as Tanisha, and he was genuinely taken aback by her. He could tell she was different and he already felt something for her.

They went to catch a movie and then grabbed dinner afterward. Once they finished eating, neither one of them was ready to go home, so Ray asked Tanisha if she wanted to go to the beach for a while. She agreed and thought to herself about how much she liked Ray. Deep down she was worried that her vow of celibacy might be a deal breaker for him. After all he was more handsome than any boy at her school and the city's star high school quarterback. She imagined how many girls there were throwing themselves at him every day and hoped that she still had a chance.

After their walk on the beach Ray drove Tanisha home.

"I had a good time tonight, you're pretty cool for a Viking Ms. Williams," Ray said as he smiled at Tanisha.

Tanisha smiled and said, "Yea whatever, you're not too bad yourself Mr. Donovan."

There was a brief moment of silence and Ray touched Tanisha's hand. After a few seconds their eyes met, and Ray leaned in for a kiss. Tanisha quickly turned her cheek and his lips landed there.

Ray was obviously a little confused and asked if he did anything wrong. Tanisha assured him that everything was great and that she enjoyed herself and then told Ray about her vow of celibacy.

"It's something that I take seriously, so I try not to put myself in situations that could compromise the promise that I made to myself and God," she said.

Ray took a few seconds to respond and Tanisha nervously waited for him to say something.

"That's something that I can respect. We don't have to have sex, but I do still want to see you again if that's ok with you," he said calmly and sincerely.

Tanisha thanked him for understanding and gave him a hug before getting out of the car. Before she walked into the house she turned around and told him to call her when he made it home.

Over the next few weeks, Tanisha and Ray got a little more serious and decided to date each other exclusively. About five months into their relationship, Ray invited Tanisha to a party that some kids from his school were throwing. Tanisha agreed to go even though she really wasn't up to it. She was in the middle of studying for her finals, but she decided it would be ok to take a little break.

Ray came to pick her up and as they arrived at the party, Tanisha got the first glimpse of what she had gotten herself into. They pulled up to a huge brick mansion and there were cars and teenagers filling the street all the way from the end of the block up to this huge house. Ray assured her that she would have a good time and took her by the hand and into the house. He introduced her to all of his friends and team mates. They all drank beer while Tanisha nursed a bottle of water.

After a bit of socializing, Ray led Tanisha to the pool area and found them two seats.

"Stay here babe, and save that seat for me, I'm going to find you some soda, and I'll be right back," Ray said as he kissed her forehead and disappeared into the crowd.

Ray was standing in the kitchen pouring Tanisha a cup of soda out of a bottle when his team mate Darren approached him.

"My man Ray! What's up dude? I saw you and your girl earlier and I've got to say she seems a little tense bro," he said while putting his arm around Ray's neck. Darren was obviously drunk.

"Oh no, she's really cool bro, she's just a little stressed about finals you know. She honestly isn't really a party girl either," he replied while picking Tanisha's drink up off the counter.

"Well, because you're my boy, and my favorite quarterback, I'm going to do you a favor." Darren's voice and the half-smile that appeared on his face made Ray uncomfortable as he spoke. Darren took his arm away from Ray's neck and fumbled into his pocket. He pulled out a balled-up paper towel and unwrapped a handful of pills.

"Whoa, what are those?" Ray asked.

Before he answered, Darren took two pills out of the pile and dropped them into Tanisha's drink.

"Calm down bro don't get all 'dare to be different' on me. It's not a big deal. These will just loosen her up, and I promise you guys will have a good time tonight," said Darren.

At this point Ray felt uneasy, but he convinced himself that it was okay. He told himself that Tanisha needed to let loose, that she'd worked too hard, and that she deserved to have fun for at least one night. He knew she would never drink the soda if she knew something was in it, so he decided he wouldn't tell her about the pills. Ray made his way back to Tanisha. She had three girls around her and Ray wondered how she had made friends that fast. Tanisha smiled at Ray as he got closer. Ray handed Tanisha the cup and grabbed his beer off of the nearby table. As he watched her drink the soda, a sick feeling crept into his stomach. Part of him wanted to stop her from drinking it, but he also wanted to see what she would be like if she really let loose and enjoyed herself. He had no idea that he had just given her a date rape drug.

Ray waited for Tanisha to finish her drink and wondered what would happen. He was on his third beer and was starting to lose the uneasy feeling he had earlier. A few moments after Tanisha finished her drink, she told Ray that she wanted to dance. They headed into the crowd and moved to the music. Ray noticed that Tanisha was a great dancer. He thought to himself that Darren was right, Tanisha was having fun. After a few moments of dancing Tanisha put her arms around Ray and began to kiss him. Ray and Tanisha had kissed plenty of times but never like this. After a few songs Tanisha told Ray that she wanted to go somewhere private. They weren't far from the beach that they went to on their first date, so Ray took her there.

They got into the back seat of Ray's car and began making out. Tanisha started to undress and in a moment of clarity Ray stopped to ask if she was sure about what she was doing. Tanisha put her hand over Ray's mouth and told him to be quiet, slurring her words. Ray was enjoying this side of Tanisha and it didn't take much to convince him not to argue with her. Just like that, the vow that Tanisha made to God, her parents, her friends, and most of all to herself, was broken.

The next morning Tanisha woke up in a daze. She couldn't understand why she didn't remember anything from the night before. She searched around for her phone and didn't see it. She figured it must have still been in her purse. As she picked up her purse from the side of her bed, her underwear from the night before fell onto the floor, and she knew something was wrong. She immediately called Ray.

"Ray, what happened last night? Please tell me I didn't break my vow Ray. Please tell me I didn't break it." Tanisha held back tears as she pleaded with Ray.

Ray was confused at first about why Tanisha didn't remember what happened between them. He eventually thought about the pills and realized that regardless of what Darren said, they were a big deal. He knew he had to come clean even if it meant the end of their relationship. He took a deep breath and told her everything.

Without saying anything else Tanisha hung up the phone. She stared blankly for a moment, trying to process everything, but she eventually broke down. She grabbed her pillow and silently sobbed into it. Once she was able to stop crying she picked up her phone to call Veronica, ignoring twenty missed calls from Ray. She had to tell someone what happened, and she knew Veronica would know what to do or say and she wasn't ready to face Jasmine yet. She told her friend what happened, and Veronica was very patient and understanding. She told Tanisha that she should have called her before she went. Kids from Ray's school were known for using different drugs, including the date rape drugs that were used on Tanisha.

After a month, Tanisha was finally starting to get back to her normal life. She came clean to Jasmine and stayed in their group at school to share her story with the younger members to teach them how to avoid certain situations. One morning Tanisha woke up with an unbearable nauseous feeling. She barely made it to the bathroom before vomiting. An overwhelming feeling of fear took her over. She immediately went to the pharmacy and bought a pregnancy test. She went to the bathroom in the store and took it right then. The test was positive, she was pregnant.

Tanisha and Ray had slowed down their relationship since the night of the party and she barely returned his calls, but in that moment, all the anger and sadness she felt boiled over and she called him.

She was so angry that she could hardly speak when he finally answered. "You. You raped me! You drugged me, and you raped me! And now I'm pregnant Ray! I wasn't even supposed to have sex until marriage, but now I'm a pregnant high school student thanks to you and your stupid friend!" she yelled and cried at the same time.

"Babe, please calm down, and don't say things like that. I would never set you up to rape you! I had no idea what those pills were, I really just wanted to see you have fun. I love you Tanisha. I love you and I want to marry you. I've never said that to anyone but I'm saying it now and I mean it."

"Marry me? What about football." Tanisha replied softly

"I can still play football just trust me. I'm going to get my mom to help us, she will understand. Where are you? We are going to come pick you up so that we can figure this out." Ray spoke in a voice that soothed Tanisha. She actually considered what he was saying, and entertained thoughts of marrying Ray. If she ended up marrying him, it wouldn't be so bad that she broke her vow early.

Tanisha headed home and waited for Ray and his mom to pick her up. When they got back to Ray's house Mrs. Donovan sat them down and they started to have a conversation. She talked to Tanisha about how hard it would be to attend college with a baby, and how it would take a "miracle" for her to achieve her goal of becoming a teacher. She said she would hate to see Tanisha throw her life away by having a baby at such a young age. Mrs. Donovan assured Tanisha that they could get married after college and then start their life together. At the end of the 90-minute conversation, Tanisha was convinced that she needed to have an abortion.

Mrs. Donovan told Tanisha that she didn't have to worry about anything, she was going to take her to get it and pay for it, so her parents would never have to know and that way they wouldn't be disappointed in her. The next morning Mrs. Donovan and Ray arrived to pick Tanisha up and they headed to the abortion clinic.

The ride was eerily quiet, and Tanisha started to have second thoughts, but she figured that it was too late. The decision had already been made. Ray and Mrs. Donovan waited in the lobby while Tanisha had her procedure. When she was done they dropped her off at home without a word.

It was her spring break, so Tanisha laid in bed for days without speaking to anyone. Her parents both went to work every day, so they didn't have time to notice that something was drastically wrong. Tanisha cried constantly and started to isolate herself from her family, her friends, and from Ray. When she returned to school she wasn't her usual upbeat self. She didn't talk to anyone, didn't raise her hand in class, and she ate lunch alone.

Her friends gave her space for about two months, but they had eventually had enough. Veronica, Trish, and Jasmine came to Tanisha's house on a Friday night and pulled her out of bed.

"You are getting out of this house, you are going to hang out with us, it's not up for debate," Trish said as she picked a dress and a pair of shoes out of Tanisha's closet.

Tanisha finally agreed to hang out with her friends, and they went to a party that some kids from their school were throwing. On the way to the party Tanisha was finally able to smile and laugh with her friends. She missed them dearly and was happy to be out of her depression. When they finally made it to the party the first, person Tanisha saw was Ray. He was in the kitchen smiling and whispering in the ear of some girl from Tanisha's school.

Tanisha's whole body grew hot with rage. The emotions from everything that she had been through over the past three months all came rushing back. Before she knew it, she was in the kitchen punching Ray in the chest and screaming, "You get me pregnant, then tell me you want to marry me, then you and your mother convince me to abort my baby, and NOW you're here trying to have sex with someone else! Really Ray? You disgust me!"

Just like that, Tanisha walked out of the party, and out of Ray's life. Tanisha's grades dropped a bit as she was wrapping up high school and preparing for college. She would rarely talk in class, and her teachers were concerned because she even began to push them away and avoid interacting with them.

Tanisha's parents found out about the abortion right before high school graduation. Tanisha's father sat her down and stated, "Sweetheart, you hold your head up high at ALL times. Your mother and I love you unconditionally and are very proud of you and all your accomplishments. We know that life will throw you some curve balls and when that happens, you can always call us and count on us for support. We've got your back, your front, and your sides. There is nothing you can do to change the fact that we love you with all our hearts. Just continue to be kind, have courage and your life will be amazing."

Seven years later, Tanisha had earned a bachelor's degree from Spellman University and a master's Degree from Howard University. Although she was very smart, Tanisha found herself getting sad a lot while in college. She would retreat to her room and engulf herself in her studies when she would feel sadness. She would also run three miles a few times a week to relieve stress. While in college at Spellman University, Tanisha attended a seminar called "Forgive, Love, and Live." The seminar gave specific instructions on how to forgive everyone in your life who has ever hurt you in any way. She learned how to effectively forgive Ray, his mother, Darren, and herself. She is currently a high school teacher and she also runs a non-profit organization that allows her to work with teens who have gone through abortions. She provides them with emotional and psychological support. She is also a well-known motivational speaker and is dedicated to helping young women build self-esteem. She now lives in Atlanta and is married to an attorney. They are expecting their second child, a boy, in three months. Tanisha and her girls from high school all remain close friends.

Ray played professional football as a back-up quarterback but was cut after only two years in the league. He went through a bit of depression after his separation from football, but eventually his high school contacted him and asked him to apply for the head coaching position. He is now a physical education teacher and the head coach at his old high school. Ray learned from the mistakes of his youth and made sure he took the time to mentor his players on how to be strong men and to live a life of purpose. Ray has two boys, ages four, and five, from a failed relationship. He is single and working on spending more time with them. He reached out to Tanisha over the years to try to let her know that he came to the realization of how horribly he treated her. He attempted to apologize but his calls were never returned.

QUESTIONS:

1. Do you think Tanisha was heartbroken and in an emotional hole BEFORE she met Ray?
   YES | NO | I'M NOT SURE

2. Do you think Tanisha was heartbroken and in an emotional hole AFTER she broke up with Ray?
   YES | NO | I'M NOT SURE

3. Which event do you think pushed Tanisha in an emotional hole?

Her high school team losing their season opener	Seeing Ray trying to have sex with another girl
Having an abortion	Finding out she was drugged
Finding out she was no longer a virgin	

4. Do you think she was in an emotional hole after she got married?
   YES | NO | I'M NOT SURE

5. What did Tanisha do to climb out of her emotional hole?

	Sought COUNSELING		Kept a daily JOURNAL
	Found PURPOSE for her life		FORGAVE everyone that ever hurt her
	Developed her SPIRITUAL life		

6. When Tanisha was in her emotional hole, which relationships do you think were affected?

	The relationship with her child
	The relationship with her significant other (Ray)
	The relationship with her parents (mom and dad)
	The relationship with her friends (Veronica, Trish, and Jasmine)
	The relationship with her leaders (teachers)

SPIRITUAL REFERENCES:

1. *"We humans keep brainstorming options and plans, but God's purpose prevails."*
   - **Proverbs 19:21 (MSG)**

2. *"Form your* purpose *by asking for counsel, then carry it out using all the help you can get."*
   - **Proverbs 20:18 (MSG)**

3. *"Put God in charge of your work, then what you've planned will take place."*
   - **Proverbs 16:3 (MSG)**

FAMOUS QUOTES:

1. *"The purpose of life is not to be happy. It is to be useful, to be honorable, to be compassionate, to have it make some difference that you have lived and lived well."*
   - **Ralph Waldo Emerson**

2. *"Carve your name on hearts, not tombstones. A legacy is etched into the minds of others and the stories they share about you."*
   - **Shannon L. Alder**

3. *"Spirituality is recognizing and celebrating that we are all inextricably connected to each other by a power greater than all of us, and that our connection to that power and to one another is grounded in love and compassion. Practicing spirituality brings a sense of perspective, meaning and purpose to our lives."*
   - **Brené Brown**

TAKEAWAYS:

1. You may have wonderful parents, attend a great church who supports you and your family, great friendships, and even a pretty decent girlfriend/boyfriend. Life can still find a way to throw a curveball and you have to be prepared, and not fall apart when it does.

2. Communicating with trusted advisors, mentors, counselors, life coaches, parents, etc. can really help us sort life out. Don't try to do it alone.

3. There is a 98% chance that you will NOT marry your high school sweetheart. Those relationships help us understand what we like and what we don't like about being in relationships. The key here is to not bring a baby into the world while you are figuring it all out. Both sides learn a lot about being independent, dependent, or co-dependent on another human being while in a relationship.

AFFIRMATIONS: (Recite each morning)

I will volunteer weekly to help others succeed (i.e., children, elderly, homeless, etc.). This will give me a sense of community, purpose, love, and becoming a beacon of light to others.

TIME TO CLIMB:

Exercise 1: FIND YOUR PURPOSE

Materials needed: Pen

The information below will help you discover your purpose in as fast as 15 minutes. What you discover as your purpose today, may change in the future as you continue to discover life and what you are actually good at, what you love to do, and discover the value you bring to others based on your life experiences.

Here are a few questions that may spark interest in what you want to do for a career and how to help others who may want to follow in your footsteps. The other five questions are designed to help you find your life's purpose.

1. If you were guaranteed success in any career field, which career field would you choose if I paid you $500,000 per year to do it?

    _____

    Note: If you know the answer to the question above, then you are very close to finding your purpose.

2. Once you start working in your dream career or building your dream business, how can you help/mentor others who may have similar dreams?

    _____

Key questions to finding your purpose:

(My personal answers are in parenthesis)

Who are you? *(Rod Cunningham)*
What do you enjoy doing and what makes you come alive? *(Mentoring, empowering, and coaching)*
Who do you enjoy doing it for? *(Teenagers and young adults)*

What do the people who you do it for want out of it? *(They want to be taught how to live an amazing life)*

What is in it for you? *(I feel fulfilled as a human being)*

My purpose statement is now complete: "Hello, my name is Rod Cunningham and I enjoy mentoring, empowering and coaching teenagers and young adults. Our young people want to be taught how to live an amazing life and this makes me feel fulfilled as a human being."

When asked, so what do you do Rod, my response is "I help young people create an amazing future for themselves."

The sooner you find your purpose in life, the sooner you will find happiness in your life. Jim Carey once said, "I think everybody should get rich and famous and do everything they ever dreamed of, so they can see it's not the answer." Living a purpose-filled life will make you extremely happy.

You may have to take a job when you are young to pay your bills and support your family, while working on your purpose part-time or as a volunteer. The idea, is to quickly look for a dream career that will align with your purpose (get someone to pay you for what you love to do, while actually helping people in the process). Then you can eventually step out and build your own dream business, where you are getting paid to help others, and finding happiness and purpose in your life. If money is no longer an object for you and your family, then volunteering to help change the life of others is even more fulfilling.

Chapter 9

JOURNALING AND ART

"As there are a thousand thoughts lying within a man that he does not know till he takes up the pen to write."

- William Makepeace Thackeray

Journaling

Keeping a daily journal can be very therapeutic. It gives you the opportunity to release ideas, thoughts, and/or emotions that are bottled-up inside that you may or may not express otherwise. Young people who experience tragic events and/or abandonment find themselves looking for answers their whole lives. They wonder, "Why did you do that to me? Why did you leave me? Why did you hurt me? Why did you say that to me?"

Our brain is constantly searching for answers to these questions. Many times, after people start journaling, they feel strong and confident enough to search for answers to the questions that have bothered them since they were 10-years-old by communicating with the person who hurt them, or if that person has passed away, they are able to search for answers from family and friends who knew them best. You normally see this in adoption situations, in a sibling's death where you never got full understanding of what happened, or if a biological parent walked out on the family for many years.

Keeping a daily journal of your thoughts and the events of your life, makes for a great way to keep a historic file of your life as only seen by you. This could make for a great movie or book that you, your children, or grandchildren may write someday.

Art Therapy

Art Therapy is a form of psychotherapy that involves free self-expression through painting, drawing, or modeling, used as a remedial activity or an aid to diagnosis. I met a lady at the premiere of a movie that I acted in. The lady was an Army veteran who was raped while in the Army. This was very traumatic for her. When she left the Army, she found herself depressed, not wanting to leave the house. She noticed that when she would take a pencil and draw a line across the paper, she would begin to feel better. She first starting drawing, then she moved into painting. She then explained how her life began to change and she began to leave the house more and become more sociable.

Do you doodle? Do you find yourself drawing lines on paper or making little characters on a paper while in class or in meetings? I have watched people in meetings, and after they doodle, it appears to help them refocus their mind on what is going on in the room. Now imagine doodling, writing, journaling, drawing, or painting for a living. You would now be happier, more excited, and more fulfilled. Now imagine teaching those things to children. Now you would find yourself living in purpose because you would help others unlock their secret place as well.

JAMES "JT"

"Man, I don't even know where to begin." JT thought to himself.

He sat back in the old desk chair in the room that he had grown up in, spinning a pencil between his fingers. A few weeks prior, his thirteen-year-old daughter Anna begged him to start an autobiography. JT lived a rough life, and Anna thought that people needed to hear his story. It all began when they watched a special on television about Wordsmith the famous rapper. Before anyone knew of Wordsmith, he was a young gang member and ended up going to prison for ten years. While he was incarcerated, he put his whole life story into a series of songs which ended up being his first album. Once Wordsmith was released, he dropped his album independently and the world embraced it. It was a true story, it was raw, it was honest, and people related to it.

JT wasn't sure how influential his story would be, but he figured writing it down would be a healthy outlet for his pain, and he would have something to leave his daughter when his time came. After staring down at an empty journal for a while, JT started to write.

"I can still smell the stale smoke and fresh liquor oozing out of my mother's pores. At an age when most children would be playing make-believe and learning how to ride a bike, I was learning how to iron clothes and re-heat pizza. My mother never came home before 10:00 pm, unless she was throwing a party for the neighborhood, so I had to make sure that I had clean clothes for school and something to eat before bed. For the most part, my mother and I lived alone, occasionally she would introduce a new boyfriend, most of them only stuck around until the liquor and drugs were gone for the month.

My relationship with my father was a lot better than the one I had with my mother, and I think she hated my father for that reason. She would tell me I looked and acted just like him and then on another day, she would tell me how much she hated him. Being a child, I took that to mean that she hated me too.

Every Wednesday and Friday, my mother threw a party for the neighborhood. When her guests started to arrive, she would always send me to my room. I would wait a few minutes and crack my bedroom door so that I could see what was going on. Eventually my mother would get too drunk to care whether I was in my room or not, so I would sneak back out into the living room. All of her parties consisted of at least four things: loud music, smoking cigarettes, drinking, and drugs. Sometimes they played "Dominos", and when the cursing started I knew it was "Spades" night.

I spent as much time as I could at my father's place as a kid. He lived with my uncles Rick and Tony, my aunt Shelby, and my four cousins "Lil" Rick, Demarcus, Antonio, and Tanya. We never had enough space at my pop's house, but to this day, I cannot remember one time that I was ready to go home when my mother would pick me up. If it were up to me, I would have stayed and ran around the neighborhood with my cousins all day, every day.

My pop was tall and strong, and he worked as a brick layer, so every time he came home he was covered in dust and sweat. Whenever my pop had a day off, we would walk to the neighborhood store and talk, he would ask me about school and teach me all the things I needed to know to grow up and be a good man like him. I can still hear his voice replaying in my mind,

"Son, you are the man of the house now, and it's your job to protect your mom. That's what men do, we protect our families. Can you promise to do that for me JT?"

Any time I made my father a promise, I had to look him in the eye and shake his hand. He would tell me that there was nothing more important than a man's word, and anytime I gave someone my word I had to deliver on the promise. When my father and I had our walks, he would buy me a frozen drink at the corner store and take me to the park to shoot hoops. Those were the times that I remember feeling like a normal kid.

When I was twelve-years-old, my pop lost his job after an argument with the head foreman on the construction site. My pop tried to find another job for months, but it seemed like every lead fell through. He would later tell me that he felt panic and desperation for the first time in his life when he checked his bank account balance to find that all he had to his name was $4.12.

My Uncle Rick saw my father's desperation and had their cousin Ray reach out to him. Ray was known as one of the biggest drug dealers in Miami. Those who were smart feared him, but everyone stayed out of his way. I can still remember the hairs standing up on the back of my neck when Ray came to speak to my pop. He pulled up the driveway in a gold Mercedes convertible with gold rims. He wore a red tracksuit and a pair of red sneakers. He left the keys in the ignition as he hopped out and told the thug that was riding with him to keep his eyes peeled. Ray flashed a smile, showing off a mouth full of gold teeth that matched all of the gold around his neck and wrists. He always gave us a handful of dollar bills when he saw us, like he was getting rid of pocket change.

"What's good lil' JT? Where's your pops?" he asked me.

Before I could answer, my father appeared in the doorway.

"Yo, Frank, come holla at me cuz." Ray said, motioning my father toward the front lawn.

My father came onto the yard and greeted his cousin Ray with a hug.

"Cuz, I heard you're goin' through it right now. I've got $4,000 I could loan you till you get back on your feet, or I've got a way that you can earn $8,000."

My pop was nervous about having any dealings with Ray because everything about him had "trouble" written all over it. Even though he had a bad feeling about what was in store for him, he was out of options and he had to do something to change his situation. Ray explained that all my pops had to do was drive a car to Georgia, drop off a package, and come back home.

My father figured the less he knew, the better. He agreed to drive the car for Ray. The next day when my mother came to pick me up, my father hugged me for a little longer than usual and told me he loved me. That was the last time that I would see him as a free man for over thirty years. My father was ten miles from the drop off point when he was pulled over. The police searched the car and found $500,000 worth of cocaine in the trunk.

My father got his prison sentence a week after my thirteenth birthday. That was the turning point in my life. My grades started to slip, and I started hanging around with kids that worked the streets for my cousin Ray. One night I came home at 2:00 AM on a school night and found my mother smoking a cigarette at the kitchen table, waiting for me.

"Come sit you're a-- down boy." The cigarette smoke flowed out of her nose and mouth as she spoke.

I sank into the chair opposite of her and stared at the kitchen floor saying nothing.

"I don't know if you're trying to end up in jail like your ignorant father, but if that's your goal you are going to reach it before you know it! I am not coming to bail your stupid a-- out of jail either! From now on you need to be in your room by the time the street lights come on!" She slammed her fist into the old wooden table as she spoke.

At that moment, I stood up from my seat and towered over my mother, and said, "You don't care about me! You always say you hate my daddy, so you hate me too! Just leave me alone and worry about your stupid drug addicted boyfriends!"

I turned my back and stormed into my room. It wasn't until I was an adult that I realized the effects that my words had on my mother. After that night we still argued, but she never brought another man into the house and only partied occasionally.

As time passed, my attitude and temper kept growing. By the time I reached my sophomore year in high school, I had a rep for fighting and my cousin Ray was starting to hear stories *about me. He would come pick me up from my mother's house and let me hang out with him and his boys. He taught me how to sell drugs, and that I had to make sure that people were scared of me at all cost. I made money and spent it on looking exactly like my cousin Ray. I filled my mouth with gold teeth and bought jewelry. I was the kid that every girl wanted, even older women in the neighborhood.*

Sophomore year was also the year that I met Shantell. She told me that she liked the fact that people knew not to mess with me, and because she was my girl they wouldn't mess with her either. I protected Shantell at all times. We had only been dating three months before we found out that she was pregnant with my daughter.

I found myself pressured to make even more money, so I asked Ray to let me do bigger jobs and because he trusted me, he did. No other drug runners were allowed to do the jobs that I was. I went on robberies, delivered drugs, and sold drugs at my school. Shantell gave birth to our daughter Anna during our senior year and I immediately fell in love with my baby girl. I loved my daughter from the first time I met her, but nothing in my brain "clicked" telling me that I needed to slow down.

One night I was at my mom's house with Shantell and Anna and I heard a knock on the door. It was Ray.

"What's good JT, come ride with your cuz for a few, I need you."

At that point in my life, making money was always my first priority. Even though I didn't want to leave my family, I knew that if I said no, Ray would never give me another big job. That was the way he operated.

"Alright, hold up cuz, I'm comin'."

Because it was a Saturday night, I already knew what was up. We were going to "The Strip" on South Beach to rob the drunk tourists. I put on a black hoodie, black jeans, and black sneakers. I kissed my daughter goodbye and hopped into the back seat of Ray's car.

We smoked marijuana and drank whiskey on the way. When we reached the beach, Ray parked in an ally and turned off the lights and ignition. We sat there and waited for someone to walk by alone. After a few moments a guy walked by the car with his head down focusing on his cell phone.

"JT that's you." Ray handed me a pistol and I pulled a ski mask out of my pocket and pulled it over my face. I got out of the car quietly and looked back at Ray and Dee before turning the corner. I walked closely behind the man and as we approached the next alley I pushed him into it and punched him in the face. Before I could even pull out my pistol I could see police lights flashing. I turned and ran back to the car yelling 'go, go, go'. Apparently, our Saturday night ritual of robbing people had caught the attention of the police, because the man I punched was an undercover officer.

Ray peeled off and headed for the interstate, after a long chase he finally stopped. Without saying anything, he looked over at Dee and grabbed his two pistols from the floor. He got out of the car and pointed them at the police shooting both guns at the same time. In a matter of seconds, I saw Ray's body falling to the ground. Just like that he was gone, at that moment I thought of Ray's five-year-old son Ray Jr., then my thoughts shifted to my own daughter and I immediately ducked and pleaded with the officers not to shoot me as they approached the car.

Because of the violence of my crime, I was charged as an adult even though I was only seventeen. I got off easy in the eyes of the law with a five-year sentence, but those five years were the darkest of my entire life. I had to fight guys off of me every single day. I was big and strong for a seventeen-year-old kid, but I was just that, a kid. I couldn't always fight them off and on the days I couldn't, I'd wish for death. They emasculated me, de-humanized me, and eventually I couldn't even recognize myself. My mother never came to visit, but Shantell brought Anna once a month. After a while, I couldn't look my daughter in the eye because of what was happening to me sexually in prison, and I asked Shantell to stop bringing her. I lied and told her that everything was okay, and that I just didn't want her to remember seeing me here.

I ended up serving three and a half years of my five-year sentence. By that time, I was a twenty-year-old shell of the thirteen-year-old that lost his father to the prison system. My parole officer warned me that if I did not find a job I would have to go back to prison and complete my sentence. There I was, a broken man, expected to go back into society, find a job, and be thankful for only getting sexually violated for three years of my life. My time in prison hardened me. I was angry, unpredictable, and all around off balance. In order to cope, when I came home I would sit in my room for hours listening to gangster rap music, playing video games, and smoking marijuana.

Shantell and my mother tried to talk to me, but I pushed them both away. I was all on my own by choice. I couldn't sleep, and I rarely talked to anyone, even my relationship with my daughter was different. I eventually found a party supply company that was willing to hire me, they paid me $13.00/hour to drive their delivery truck.

Working actually made me start to feel a little better about myself. I had less time on my hands and I was able to do things for my daughter. I spent the weekends with her and when it was hot out, I took her to the neighborhood store for a frozen drink, just like my father had done for me. "

JT continued his autobiography throughout the next six months and since he had learned to draw in prison, he ended each chapter with a sketch to represent the era of his life that the chapter referenced. JT was thirty- years-old when he decided to start writing his book. He still worked at the party supply store and spent weekends with his daughter. When Anna was at her mom's house, JT would wake up at 6:00 AM and go to work and come home at about 8:00 PM. He was still living in his mother's house, and just like when he was a child, they rarely spoke. He would come home, turn on his music, and fade away into his video games.

As he got further along in his book, he found himself not touching his games for weeks at a time. He would write in a personal journal and choose entries from it to put into the book. After releasing all of his pain and emotions into the words he was writing, he started to actually feel something shift inside of him, he felt normal, and one day he even approached his mother.

He would always make his coffee and go about his day, only speaking to his mother when necessary. He decided that this particular Sunday morning would be different.

"Uh, hey ma' I'm about to make some coffee, you want some."

His mother seemed startled that he had spoken more than two words to her.

"Yes son, thank you,"

They ate breakfast together and talked more than they had in years. JT told his mother about the book that he was working on and she seemed genuinely impressed. Their relationship got better with time, Ray told his mother all the things that hurt him as a child and his mother listened and even apologized. Ray thought fixing the relationship that he had with his mother would be impossible, but there they were, finally in a good place after so many years.

JT's life was finally going in the right direction, he came out of his shell, got promoted to supervisor at his job and began dating a woman named Tasha. After two years of journaling and working on his book, JT started attending church with Tasha and Anna. Sometimes his mother even came. Anna bragged to everyone she knew about how her father was writing a book. One day after church JT met one of the youth pastors.

"Hey, Brother, good afternoon. My name is Pastor Aaron, I work over in the youth ministry." Pastor Aaron said while extending his hand.

"Hi Pastor, I'm JT how are you, Sir?" JT replied giving him a firm handshake.

That day, the pastor told JT that Anna told him about the book. Pastor Aaron had contacts at a publishing company and told JT that he would be happy to try to offer some help with publishing. After three months of intense focus, the book was finally ready to be published.

For the first nine months, sales were slow, but JT was content if his story helped motivate at least one person. JT was living his life, still working at the party supply store as a supervisor, and he eventually got himself an apartment. He was content with life. One day, surprisingly, JT received a phone call from a producer in Los Angeles who wants to turn his book into a movie. JT was ecstatic, and Anna was the first person he called.

"Baby girl! We did it! We did it!" He was overcome with emotion and could barely get the words out.

JT explained what was going on to Anna and she burst into tears telling him that she always knew he could do it. JT went through six months of negotiations with the film production company before they could come to an agreement. At the age of thirty-one, JT became a millionaire. He was paid $4 million for the rights to his story. JT never stopped journaling and through that alone, he brought himself out of depression, and was finally able to live up to the life that his father wanted for him. He proposed to Tasha and they are planning to get married in the spring. Anna is a happy fifteen-year-old and thrives in school and sports. JT purchased a new home for his mother and she has finally found the happiness she was looking for throughout her life with her new fiancé Peter. JT visits his father Frank every week and is awaiting his release.

QUESTIONS:

1. If JT was in an emotional hole, do you think his hole was shallow or deep?
   SHALLOW | DEEP | I HAVE NO IDEA

2. Do you think going to prison pushed him deeper in his emotional hole?
   YES | NO | I'M NOT SURE

3. Do you think the abuse he encountered in prison pushed him even deeper in his emotional hole?   YES | NO | I'M NOT SURE

4. Once JT left prison, which relationships do you think were affected because of his emotional hole?

	The relationship with his child (Anna)
	The relationship with his significant other (Shantell)
	The relationship with his parents (mom)
	The relationship with his friends
	The relationship with his employer (Party Supply Company)

5. Many times, we choose vices (see Table 1-1) that appear normal because we saw others in our family with the same vice or it is a vice that is most acceptable in our particular community. In other words, my dad drank, so I drank. My mom smoked marijuana, so it's OK for me to smoke. Those familiar family vices are considered normal and most accepted by parents, siblings, uncles, aunts, cousins, etc. Many times, these vices are considered "no big deal". Which vice do you think JT picked up from his mother or father?

Alcohol	Sexual promiscuity
Gambling	Pornography
Marijuana	Cigarettes

SPIRITUAL REFERENCES:

1. *"Then the Lord answered me and said: "Write the vision And make it plain on tablets, That he may run who reads it."*
   - **Habakkuk 2:2 (NKJV)**

2. *"Thus speaks the Lord God of Israel, saying: 'Write in a book for yourself all the words that I have spoken to you.'"*
   - **Jeremiah 30:2 (NKJV)**

FAMOUS QUOTES:

1. *"Keep a notebook. Travel with it, eat with it, sleep with it. Slap into it every stray thought that flutters up into your brain. Lead pencil markings endure longer than memory."*
   - **Jack London**

2. *"In the journal I do not just express myself more openly than I could to any person; I create myself. The journal is a vehicle for my sense of selfhood. It represents me as emotionally and spiritually independent. Therefore (alas) it does not simply record my actual, daily life but rather — in many cases — offers an alternative to it."*
   - **Susan Sontag**

3. *"Fill your paper with the breathings of your heart."*
   - **William Wordsworth**

4. *"I consider that portion of my life which has been spent in keeping journals and writing history to have been very profitably spent."*
   - **Wilford Woodruff**

5. *"I make art when I can't gather the words to say."*
   - **Nikki Rowe**

6. *"Imagination is tapping into the subconscious in a form of open play. That is why art or music therapy, which encourages a person to take up brushes and paint or an instrument, and just express themselves, is so powerful."*
   - **Phil 'Philosofree' Cheney**

TAKEAWAYS:

1. Pressure can make a pipe burst. We can't hold life's problems and negative emotions inside of us for long periods because eventually they will come out. Normally, this comes out as anger and anxiety which could lead to screaming and fighting.

2. If you find yourself frustrated, living in an emotional hole, it is important to CHOOSE to make good decisions, establish new friendships, and change your surroundings, if you want to avoid trouble with law enforcement. If you CHOOSE to make bad decisions that inevitably put you in jail, please understand that you won't be the only one going to jail. You are putting everyone you love in an emotional jail cell with you, your parents, grandparents, children, significant other, friends, etc., most of whom have tried to talk you into staying out of trouble. They are all sitting around trying to figure out why you wouldn't listen to anyone. They have to pay money for your attorney, which takes food off of the table. They have to pay the high phone bill just so that you can call home and talk. They have to raise your child, who will be angry with you because you abandoned them. Your kids will always wonder why they were NOT important enough for you to stay out of trouble.

AFFIRMATIONS: (Recite each morning)

   - I will keep a journal by writing down my thoughts and daily events.

TIME TO CLIMB:

Exercise 1: START TO JOURNAL

Materials needed: Pen and journal from a dollar store

1. Open a blank page in your journal and write down today's date.

2. You can start by breaking up your thoughts in three sections (morning, noon, and night). Ask yourself, what happened this morning, what did I do, how did it make me feel, what did I learn? Do the same thing around noon time and again at night before bed.

3. If you can start by writing down what happened the last couple of days prior, that would also be effective.

4. Make entries every day. At the end of the month, be sure to read it in its entirety. You will be surprised at what you wrote about yourself.

Exercise 2: LOVE IN ACTION

Materials needed: Pen

Exercise 1: LOVE

1. Break up into groups of three.

2. Read the definition of love and discuss each section.

   Love is patient, love is kind. It does not envy, it does not boast, it is not proud. It does not dishonor others, it is not self-seeking, it is not easily angered, it keeps no record of wrongs. Love does not delight in evil but rejoices with the truth. It always protects, always trusts, always hopes, always perseveres.

3. What does each section mean?

   a. Love is patient: _____

   _____

b. Love is kind: _____

_____

c. It does not envy: _____

_____

d. It does not boast: _____

_____

e. It is not proud: _____

_____

f. It does not dishonor others: _____

_____

g. It is not self-seeking: _____

_____

h. It is not easily angered: _____

_____

i. It keeps no record of wrongs: _____

_____

j. Love does not delight in evil but rejoices with the truth:

_____

_____

k. It always protects, always trusts, always hopes, always perseveres:

_____

_____

Chapter 10

YOUR CHARACTER

"Nearly all men can stand adversity, but if you want to test a man's character, give him power."

- Abraham Lincoln

When we act out or shut out, we may participate in activities that are harmful to our five most important relationships (relationships with our children, spouse, parents, best friend, and supervisors). It is also important to know that we also have good qualities that we can build upon.

Your Good Qualities

The list below are some important qualities of someone who has a good heart: (Check all that apply to you currently)

Table 10-1

Shows empathy	Says words like, - *"I don't know what to say to you, but I am glad you shared your pain with me. I am here if you need me".* - *"Let me help you. I've been in the same hole that you are in and I am willing to get in with you."*
Shows sympathy	Says words like "I'm sorry your dog died, BUT you can always get a new dog." They are concerned for a moment, then life must go on. I prefer empathy over sympathy.
Good manners	Will hold doors for others, speak or wave to people in passing, and respects the space and belongings of others.
Shows kindness	Places phone call often to check on friends and family.
Responsive to others	Responds to emails, texts, or phone calls in a timely manner.
Shows love to others	Tells parents, friends, siblings, and the important people in their life that they love them prior to getting off the phone or leaving their presence.
Respectful of others	Use words like, "Excuse me" and "May I."

	Respectful of authority	Uses words like, "Yes Ma'am," or "Yes Sir."
	Donates time to causes	Volunteers in the community.
	Willing to help a person in need	Will give someone a ride if they see them walking or at a bus stop.
	Listens to the needs of others	Listens to others without interrupting them.
	Cares about what happens to others	Will call a friend to check to see if they are OK after a sickness.
	Able to keep secrets of others	Will not spread gossip about someone else who maybe experiencing problems in their life.
	Looks for ways to help and/or mentor others	Will go out of their way to mentor others by volunteering to help them become successful in life and in business.
	Grateful attitude	Uses words like, "Thank you, please, and I appreciate you."
	Dependable	Shows up at work and to meetings on time.
	Does what they say	Keeps their word.
	Good Character	Honest, courageous, loyal, ethical, and lives by a moral code.
	Honorable	Strives to live a life worth emulating and respects our military and law enforcement. Believes in truth and fairness.
	Shows Integrity	They will always do what is right, even when no one else is looking.

QUESTIONS:

1. How do you define character?

_____

_____

2. Why is it important to be a person of character?

_____

_____

3. Do you consider yourself to be trustworthy? _____

4. How many areas were you able to check off in Table 10-1? _____

Your Development

To become successful in your personal, professional, and spiritual life, it is important to do the following for self-development:

Table 10-2

	Find a Mentor		Develop Your Mind Daily
	Forgive Yourself and Forgive Others who may have hurt you in the past		Accept Responsibility for the Good and Bad in your life
	Develop a Vision Board		Create Four Personal Pillars of Trust
	Develop an attitude of gratitude		Formal Education
	Develop 15-20 Daily Affirmations		Become an Avid Reader
	Develop short and long-term goals		Feed your spirit man
	Manage Expectations w/everyone you love		Become a Saver/Investor and not a Spender

Formal Education

Many young, and some old, feel as though college is a hard accomplishment. College work is not hard, but it requires focus, commitment, and the ability to organize your time, your activities, and your life. If you can get through high school, then you are smart enough to get through college. Some young people don't attend college because they can't afford it, or they have to get a job because of their responsibilities (i.e., spouse, kids, sick parent, etc.). I would ask that all high school students consider auditing a college class. They will find that the material is not difficult, and it will give a since of ease as they prepare for life after high school.

Table 10-3

Associates Degree	Two-year (30 credit-hours): course of study from a junior college, technical college, vocational college or university. Some Associate of Arts (AA) or Associates of Science (AS) degrees are focused on specific subject areas and some are general studies in preparation for a bachelor's degree. *Average 2016 salary = $45K*
Bachelor's Degree	Four or five-year (60+ credit-hours): Undergraduate course of study from a college or university. Bachelor of Arts (B.A.) and Bachelor of Science (B.S.) *Average 2016 salary = $70K*
Master's Degree	Two-Year (40 credit-hours): Graduate course of study from a college or university. Graduates possess advanced knowledge of a specialized body of applied and theoretical topics. *Average 2016 salary = $100K (part-time college instructors add $40K)*
Doctoral Degree	Four – eight years (60-120 semester hours): The Doctorate degree is the most advanced degree you can earn, symbolizing that you have mastered a specific area of study or field of profession. *Average 2016 salary = $140K+ (part-time college professors add $70K)*

QUESTIONS:

1. Do you have a mentor? Yes | No | I'm Looking for One

2. Do you think that it is OK to have multiple mentors? Yes | No | Maybe

3. Who is responsible for your SUCCESS in High School, College and in LIFE?

	My teachers		Law enforcement officers
	My parents		The mayor
	My siblings		The economy (i.e., more jobs)
	My significant other		I AM!
	The government (i.e., free grants, welfare, etc.)		The President

4. Who has the power to derail your success and stop you from achieving your goals?

	My teachers		Law enforcement officers
	My parents		The mayor
	My siblings		The economy (i.e., more jobs)
	My significant other		I DO!
	The government (i.e., free grants, welfare, etc.)		The President

5. Have you toured any colleges as a potential student?   YES | NO
   If Yes, which ones? _____

   _____

   Note: College visits can start as early as ten-years-old. There are many city-wide programs that can take you on a college tour for free. Ask your school's counselor for assistance.

6. Which College do you plan to attend?   _____

Increase Your Knowledge

By renewing your mind through reading and learning new things, you can open up a world that you never knew existed. You can become very powerful by becoming a reader. The person with the knowledge has the power. Books are considered vital tools in your personal SUCCESS TOOLBOX.

At a minimum, the books below should be on your bookshelf at all times for quick access, in the mean time you can find some audio titles on YouTube for free:

Table 10-4

1. *"The 7 Habits of Highly Effective People,"* Stephen R. Covey	5. *"Rich Dad, Poor Dad,"* Robert Kiyosaki
2. *"Think and Grow Rich,"* Napoleon Hill	6. *"The 5 Love Languages,"* Gary Chapman
3. *"As a Man Thinketh,"* James Allen	7. *"The 5 Love Languages for Teens,"* Gary Chapman
4. *"Lincoln on Leadership,"* Abraham Lincoln	8. *"The Seven Spiritual Laws of Success,"* Deepak Chopra

Other book recommendations:

_____

_____

_____

Allowing negative people and negative conversations in our lives can be devastating to our personal growth. We must guard ourselves from these people until we are mentally strong enough to tell them that we are not interested in having a conversation if it is not going to be positive. This is not to say that we must run from our problems or stick our heads in the sand and wish it away, but it is about being in a "solution oriented mindset." If we are going to have a negative conversation, then a component of the conversation must be on how to come up with a solution. Listening to motivational speakers is a way to combat the negative things that our mind may turn to from time to time. If we listen to a positive motivational message every morning before we attend work or school, it can make a major difference in our attitude for the day.

Chapter 11

INFORMATION FOR PARENTS, STEP-PARENTS, TEACHERS, MENTORS, AND LAW ENFORCEMENT

PARENTS, STEP-PARENTS AND GUARDIANS

According to the book, *Growing Up with a Single Parent*, by Sara McLanahan,

> *A weakened father-child relationship can undermine a child's trust in both parents and increase their uncertainty about the future, making the child more difficult to manage. In families where the mother remarries or cohabits with an adult male, the quality of parenting is still likely to be lower than in families with two biological parents. From the child's point of view, having a new adult move into the household creates another disruption. Even when a stepfather tries to play an active role in parenting the child, his efforts may be rejected or undermined by the mother because she is reluctant to share authority or because she does not trust his judgement. Children may reject their stepfathers because they resent having to share their mothers, or because they feel loyalty toward their fathers, or because they secretly hope their biological parents will get back together.[06]*

Many children want their biological parents to be in the same home so that they can feel whole, comforted, and loved by the two-people responsible for their birth. Some kids view the step-parent as an obstacle to having that whole family structure and will act out or shut out accordingly. This is how we are wired and there is no need for the step-parent, grand-parent, or adoptive parent to get offended. Parents should address each concern with the child and explain the situation without speaking negatively about the other biological parent or the biological parent's new spouse.

For Example:

Parent: Sweetheart, I've noticed that you get frustrated when my boyfriend is in your presence. Is everything OK?

Child: I'm fine.

Parent: Do you want to talk about it?

Child: Not really.

Parent: Well, I recently read that children your age feel as though a boyfriend means that I will spend less time with you, that you feel as though my new boyfriend is blocking your father and I from getting back together, or you feel that you have to look out for your father by rejecting my boyfriend. Do you feel that any of these things apply to you?

Child: Well, now that you mention it, I do feel that if you have a boyfriend, then you and dad will never get back together.

Parent: Well, sweetheart, unfortunately your dad and I made an adult decision that breaking up was the best thing for both of us. Sometimes, people grow apart, or they change during a marriage. The chances of your father and I getting back together is very slim at this point and my boyfriend has nothing to do with it. He is a great guy, and I want you to try to give him a chance to prove it to you. You and your father can still have an excellent relationship, but you have to let your father know what you expect from him. Don't keep things bottled up. If you have concerns, let's sit down and talk about it. I love you and I am very proud of you.

What I have found is that an awesome step-parent does the following:

    a. Provides love, acceptance, and encouragement to the child/children
    b. Provides patience and understanding of the child's need to bond with BOTH of their biological parents (whether the other parent pays child support or not).
    c. Provides love and support to their own biological children from other relationships. They may view you as a hypocrite if you don't spend time with all your children.

We all want to have a good relationship with our biological parents, whether they live with us or not. For a step-father, in particular, I have found that he may work closely with his step-son to teach him how to be an honorable man, how to develop friendships, how to play sports, how to do better in school, and how to treat women to include their mom and sisters. But, when the biological father visits, the son may find himself very excited about the visit and impressing his father, causing him to perform better at a basketball/football game, and wanting to spend all of his time with the biological father during the visit. Although the step-father may feel slighted in this scenario, I am sharing this to say that the son's feelings and yearning to be accepted and loved by his biological father has nothing to do with how awesome the step-father has been to the son. These are two separate needs in the son's life; the need to have someone teach him about manhood and love him, and the need to be loved and accepted by the person responsible for his birth. So, step-fathers, please don't get offended and pull back from your step-children based on their interaction with their biological father. It is obvious that you do more for the child if the child lives with you, which goes without saying. Continue to step up and be that great leader for your children, your step-children, their friends, the kids in the community, and your nieces and nephews. Everyone is counting on you to succeed as a leader and be the great man that you are. Additionally, step-parents, please do not introduce your children as your step-children. It creates a line in the sand that says you are not a whole person in my life. Just simply say, "This is my son Ryan".

If the child is naturally a daddy's girl/boy, then they need 75% of their unconditional love to come from their biological father. They will need only 25% of their unconditional love to come from their biological mother.

If the child is naturally a momma's boy/girl, then they will need 75% of their unconditional love to come from their biological mother and only 25% of their unconditional love to come from their biological father.

In my case, I was naturally a momma's boy. My biological father died two weeks before I was born. Because I was only missing 25% of what I needed from my father, I did not act out too much. I could have gotten half of that 25%, (about 10-12%) of what I needed in a man, from a step-father, uncle, coach, grandfather, mentor, minister, etc., but I got very little mentorship from a man when I was growing up. I can vividly remember at the age of fourteen -years-old when my mom asked me if everything was okay with me. I told her that I felt depressed and sad for some reason and didn't understand where the sadness was coming from. Now I understand that I was simply missing my father and the continual presence of a man in my life who would guide me.

My mom was a great mom who was very loving and attentive. She never yelled at me, she hadn't spanked me since I was seven-years-old, she always told me that she was proud of me, and we never had a major argument or disagreement. She spoiled me with material things, and if I did something stupid, she would sit me down and talk to me. Yet I still felt sad for short periods between fourteen and seventeen-years-old. Although I received all of the love, acceptance, and support that any mother can give her son, I actually realized at the age of forty-six-years-old, that my acting out as a teenager (sexual promiscuity, stealing, exaggerating my achievements, etc.) was from me missing that 25% of what I needed from my biological father. "I couldn't be a man unless I could see a man." Fortunately for me, watching the junior and senior non-commissioned officers in the Air

Force was where I saw men of dignity, honor, valor, and character, leading me to model myself after them. The military mentors taught me how to love my family, work hard, and honor my country.

Although I was an only child, I can only imagine if I had an older brother who was naturally a daddy's boy, needing 75% of his unconditional love to come from his biological father. My older brother would have grown up without his father because my father would have died when my brother was just two-years-old. My brother would have possibly been labeled with ADHD because he wasn't getting the emotional support he needed from his father. He may have picked up some heavy vices as a teenager; dealing with anger and sadness, smoking marijuana and drinking heavily. All the while, people would have said, "Rod, why are you and your brother so different. Why does he get in so much trouble, yet you run away from it? He loves to fight, and you don't. You listen to your mom and take her advice, but he doesn't."

I hope you are getting the picture here. Although we would have grown up in the same household with the same kind, caring, and loving mother, my brother would have gotten in more trouble because he needed his father in his life. Each child needs something different from their biological parents. For my fictitious older brother, he may or may not have taken well to a step-father. A caring, loving, understanding step-father could have given him HALF of what he needed from a man, around 35% or so, but he would still be missing the other 40% that he so desires from his biological father. The good news here is that I have laid out in this book how a child in this scenario can take back his/her life through forgiveness, counseling, spiritual development, finding life's purpose, and journaling.

As a teenager, it is important to support the decisions of your parents, especially as it relates to new relationships. Just like you want love and companionship from your friends or girlfriend/boyfriend, your parents want love and companionship from a mate.

God didn't want Adam to be alone, so he created Eve. We were not made to be alone, especially men. For example, whenever the most hardened criminal gets in trouble in prison, he is placed in solitary confinement. Days later he is found in the fetal position upon his release from solitary confinement. From my personal observation, I have noticed that most men quickly seek out a mate when they are lonely, while *some* women cry when they feel alone. Not to say that women are helpless, but because many were taught to wait for the man to find them, not to go out and find a man. My point here is that men seek, and they seek quickly.

We were designed by God to have a companion and to show love to one another. A whole community can change overnight based on showing love and respect for God, family, careers, community, and country. With that said, if your parents have made very adult decisions and decided that they can no longer be together as a couple, then as a teenager, you must respect that adult decision, just like you want adults to respect your teenage decisions. When your parents decide that they no longer want to be alone and start dating, which may lead to marriage, you should give your blessing, allowing them to be happy. If you allow your mother or father to be happy with their new companion, then happiness flows throughout the house. You've heard the saying, "If momma's happy, everybody's happy."

If your new step-parent represents discipline that you never had, trust me when I say that "controlled" discipline is a great thing. Don't resist discipline, because we all need balance as a teenager, and a good dose of discipline can balance out love and acceptance. If you see a five-year-old running in the grocery store laughing, kicking people, and pulling food off of the shelves, what is your first thought?

Did you think, "Where are the parents? What type of upbringing does this kid have? Is there any discipline going on in this family?" You don't think about whether the child was loved and accepted, you wonder about the discipline.

Your support, kindness, respect, and love are vital when your parents begin dating again or if they decide to get married to someone else. Try hard not to isolate yourself or show anger or disrespect towards your parent or step-parent. Be supportive.

The other issue that some pre-teens/teenagers have is when their mom and step-father have children together. The natural bond of love and admiration that a three to five-year-old son or daughter has with their biological father can appear as favoritism to the older child who never experienced that bonding with their own biological father or no longer experiences it. To the step-child, this can appear to be favoritism displayed to their younger sibling. This can also happen when the teenager visits their biological father who has five and six-year-old children who seems to garner all of their dad's attention by saying, "Daddy, daddy, look at me." If the teenager experiences this in their own home, AND when they visit their father, it can cause them to shut down or become angry at both fathers in their lives.

If your parents have decided to move on and not stay together, it is not your fault, and you can make a difference by respecting the rules and the authority of the household, even when you don't agree with the decisions that are being made. Trust me when I tell you that you will have plenty of time to make your own decisions when you become an adult.

Being an exceptional step-parent is a subject matter that is large and can fill the pages of its very own book.

The most important thing to remember for adults, when you are dating or married to someone who already has children, is that **RELATIONSHIP COMES BEFORE PUNISHMENT!!!** When a child knows that he or she is loved and accepted by the step-parent, then they will follow your lead and they will know that the punishment is necessary for order and discipline in the house. The biggest complaint that a child has with their mother's boyfriend/new husband or father's girlfriend/new wife, is that they never attempted to develop a loving relationship. Yet, they are always trying to influence the punishment for non-compliance. For example, a step-father might say, "The problem is that he needs a belt to his butt and you need take him off the football team." Well, if that type of punishment is new to the child and the child hears that you, the step-father, recommended the punishment, then the child will resent you because you haven't created a relationship of love and acceptance before punishment.

It is not hard to bond with a step-child. It will take time, acceptance, patience, and love. Don't say that you don't understand the child because if you read this book, you will understand exactly what is wrong with the child, especially if a biological parent is battling with sickness, in jail, deceased, abusive, or just not active in their lives.

Here are a few tips on bonding with a step-child/adoptive child: Find genuine interest in what they enjoy doing. If the child plays video games, take an hour and sit down and play with them. If the child loves to play sports, consistently attend their games and get tickets to a professional or college game and take them (just the two of you). If the child loves reading, find out what book they are reading and go purchase the same book and read ahead, then discuss the characters in the book and what you think about the book. If the child loves to sing or dance, enroll them in classes and attend their recitals, encouraging them to succeed. If these things don't seem to work, just keep telling them that you love them and that you are proud of them. Love works every time. All of these things are part of what being a parent is all about. Again, this takes time, acceptance, patience, and love. Your children will get your time, one way or another, for example, time spent running back and forth to the school due to bad behavior or time spent visiting/bailing them out of jail, so make the time you spend with them "good time."

Book Recommendation:

The 5 Love Languages of Teenagers: The Secret to Loving Teens Effectively, by Gary Chapman

MENTORS

"A mentor is someone who sees more talent and ability within you, than you see in yourself, and helps bring it out of you."

— Bob Proctor

Mentoring simply means to advise or train someone, usually younger in experience. Mentoring is an important aspect of society, business, and the military today. Mentoring is the fastest way to success in any field because it can save time, money, and frustration when someone is attempting to achieve a goal, complete a project, or just fit-in better to a new environment. We should all have a mentor that we speak with at least twice per month, sharing our dreams and goals. Additionally, the mentor can help you design a success plan for your relationship and career.

Student Mentors:
Mentoring should start as early as possible. Fifth-graders should be assigned as a mentor to a third-grader. Eighth-graders should be assigned to mentor kids from a nearby elementary school. High school juniors and seniors should be assigned to mentor freshman. This is not only good for the mentee, but it gives responsibility and purpose to the mentor.

Adult Mentors
There are men and women who have influence, and the young people in the community would love to hear from you. If you read this entire book, you will have to tools you need to successfully mentor a teenager, a young adult, and even an old adult, helping them to achieve a better life and a prosperous future.
To find young people to mentor, simply call your local elementary, middle, or high school to find out what programs are in place for you to attach yourself to. In St. Petersburg, FL and Miami, FL, we have the 5000 Role Models of Excellence program. There are opportunities to mentor young men and women in juvenile detention centers, orphanages, prisons, after-school programs, etc.

Just remember that everyone wants to be loved unconditionally. Here are a few tips:

- Tell young people that you love them (like a brother/sister) and are proud of them

-- If you don't tell them you love them, Bo or the gangs will

- Empathize with them and do not judge young people if you want to reach them

-- Get in the hole with them and show them how to get out—Be Authentic!

- Do not yell at them

- Do not speak negatively about their parents

SCHOOL TEACHERS AND COUNSELORS

"People won't care how much you know until they know how much you care."

– Teddy Roosevelt

You can be the most intelligent educator on the planet, but until I know that you care about me and that you care about my learning and success, I can care less about how smart and educated you are.

Moms and dads are the first and second mental health (healthy mind) counselors for their children. Unfortunately, teachers become the third counselor. If a mom or dad is missing from the life of the child, home life can be chaotic for one or more of the children in that home. You as the teacher, may become the first or second healthy mind counselor for that child. Yes, I know, you didn't sign up for this, but unfortunately, this is the world that we live in today.

As you have already realized from reading this book, many of our young people have experienced childhood trauma (inappropriate touching, domestic violence, homelessness, divorce, alcohol abuse, death of a sibling/parent/friend, etc.). Many times, the memory of this trauma can be triggered by your senses (touch, smell, sight, hearing, and taste). For example, the smell of apple pie may remind a child of their grandmother because she baked apple pies often, but she also died recently. This could trigger uncontrollable crying or sadness by the student and they may not even realize why.

My point here is that many times, the school administration will punish a child based on their behavior instead of peeling back the onion and attempting to change how the child processes their feelings.

Here are a few questions that can uncover some issues facing the child (in your nicest, most concerned voice):

- Wow, are you OK?

- What's going on?

- What emotions do you feel right now?
  (i.e. fear, anger, sadness, disgust, anxious, grief, scared, etc.)

- Why do you think you feel these emotions?

- Did anything happen to you to make you feel this way?

- Do you remember the very first time that you ever felt like this in the past? How old were you?

- You don't have to tell me the details, but are you able to look back at that event that made you _____ (bad emotion) and learn anything *positive* from it?

This little exercise can be the start of young people looking for a *"learning opportunity"* in everything that happens to them. The idea is to get them to talk and realize the learning for themselves. This can become a very powerful coping strategy.

The previous example was for a child as it relates to their behavior toward themselves. The Restorative Practices® is a philosophy designed to minimize or eliminate out-of-school suspensions. Below are questions to ask during a Restorative Practices® session that many schools use as an intervention with students who are in conflict with one another. Restorative practices are done in a circle and can be practiced with two feuding students or students, parents, and life coaches when appropriate. Bring all parties together, sit in a circle, and allow only one person at a time to speak, then in a calm, concerned tone, ask each student involved in the conflict the following questions:

1. What happened?
2. What were you thinking at the time?
3. What have your thoughts been since?
4. Who has been affected by what you did?
5. In what way, have they been affected?
6. What do you think you need to do to make things right?

This process takes 5-20 minutes to resolve a conflict that could otherwise turn ugly when outside family members or friends get involved in a school issue that is mostly based on a misunderstanding due to bad communications skills between teenagers.

The Restorative Approach[07] allows students the following opportunities:

1. A chance to tell their side of the story and feel heard
2. To understand better how the situation happened
3. To understand how it can be avoided another time
4. To feel understood by the others involved
5. To find a way to move on and feel better about themselves

POLICE AND YOUTH

Police officers perform an important function in our society. They are charged with maintaining law and order, while keeping us safe. Since a small percentage of citizens actually break the law, it is very important for officers to build solid relations with the citizens who they serve.

Police officers should be required to become mentors of youth in their community. Some of our young people are scared of police officers because they have seen or heard of innocent situations turning bad or deadly. Some young people run away when stopped by a police officer, although they have done nothing wrong. We as adults know that running is a bad idea and it could lead to the perception of the involvement of illegal activity, but each person has their own perceptions of police and crime based on their history, perceptions, and cultural norms.

Our police/sheriff's offices must have open dialog with the youth in their respective communities. They must continue to be a positive presence at schools, mentoring at community centers, and visiting boy's/girl's homes to encourage positive behavior and to let the young people know that they care about them. I really enjoyed a skit by police officers and high school students called Trading Places in Chicago where they switched roles on stage during a school assembly. As the four police officers (played by the teens) were trying to calm down the situation, the seven or so teens (played by the officers) continued to call them names, shoved cell phone video cameras in their faces, and kept saying, "We don't have to do anything, we haven't broken the law." The exercise actually helped the teens see what it feels like to be police officers who are met with resistance. These type of community interventions will help the teen learn how to de-escalate, and the importance of doing so quickly.

As I sat and watched police brutality videos for two hours straight on Social Media recently, I found that many police situations get out of hand due to easily agitated (emotional) citizens and easily agitated (emotional) officers. Some, not all, police officers assume a position of "do as I say, or things will go bad for you very quickly, because I have a badge and a gun." For some officers, it was as if they were anticipating non-compliance by anyone they stopped, Black, White, Hispanic, Middle Eastern, etc. Since it is a fact that African-Americans are disproportionally stopped by police more than any other race, it is appropriate to say that there will be more African-Americans who will get agitated or emotional, which will lead to more African-American arrests.

I watched one video recently where an African-American male around twenty-one-years-old was walking in the bicycle lane on a busy street instead of walking on the sidewalk. The officer could have pulled over, rolled down his window, and requested that the man move to the sidewalk. Instead, the officer parked, turned on his police lights, got out of the car, grabbed the man by the arm, asked him where he was going, and told him that he shouldn't be walking in the street. The man quickly got agitated and yelled, "Why do you have your hands on me? Take your hands off of me! I didn't do anything. Leave me the F--- alone." The situation escalated into the man being handcuffed, put in the police car, and eventually given a ticket to appear in court for public disturbance. The officer could have escalated the charges even further by saying that the man was resisting arrest or that he assaulted the officer, but the officer recognized that there were two people on the sidewalk recording the entire incident on their smart phones. This situation could have easily led to jail time for a man who was simply walking to the mall.

Now that everyone carries a cell phone video camera in their pocket, it is no longer the word of the officer against the citizen. This has caused the very small percentage of bad police officers to check their motives and to respect the rights of all citizens, no matter their race, creed, sexual orientation, religion, etc., because unfortunately, bad police officers do exist and although the number is small, I would hate to be the one who is stopped by "that" officer. Most are good officers and they joined the police force to make a difference in their community.

Additionally, I am concerned that the criminal justice system is still designed to arrest black, brown, and poor white Americans at an alarming rate. I was in a drug courtroom recently in Tampa, Florida, where I witnessed a judge send 105 poor people to jail or prison within 7 hours, at a rate of 4 minutes per person, due to them committing a non-violent crime of drug use, not robbery, not murder, not assault, but drug use. Our young people are hurting themselves through drug use, mostly because of some sort of childhood trauma that put them in an emotional hole. When will our justice system begin to help people get out of the hole by providing counseling and coaching to develop a healthy mind, healthy body, and healthy spirit? During my time in the court room, I noticed that each detainee who had a father AND mother present (who was dressed professionally) in the courtroom and who were willing to enter their child into a drug treatment facility, was met with leniency from the judge. Those detainees without support were locked up at a rate of 20 to 1 for their non-violent crimes.

The system continues to just lock them up, pushing them deeper in their hole. Not to mention the effects imprisonment has on the children of the incarcerated who are being diagnosed with ADHD, having problems with anxiety, hating the system that locked up their parents, and continuing the generational cycle of poverty that can extend for another 60 years before the cycle is broken in their family.

African-American and Latino Police Chiefs and Sheriffs cannot stop this broken system from targeting black, brown, and poor Americans. The system is much bigger than they are. This is an effort that must be taken on by our lawmakers (politicians), the very people that we vote into office. We all must be educated about the laws that affect us, our family, and our communities, to include the community you grew up in. We must go back to those communities even though we were able to rise above those circumstance due to the strong coping skills and mentorship that allowed us to deal with adversary and bounce back to live a better life than most.

The prison systems are big business and they need warm bodies. To house a juvenile in the state of Florida for one year costs the state over $70,000. Now multiply that times 20,000 children and you have $1.4 Billion in revenue going to a private prison contracting company. Since many of the juvenile detention centers are privatized, would it be in the best interest of that billion-dollar company to have lobbyist to ensure the politicians are writing laws to keep young people incarcerated? If we look at this properly, those billions can still be generated by helping our community CLIMB out of their emotional hole. When you have healthy emotions, you are kinder and more level headed when dealing with your children, your spouse, your parents, and your employers. When people are happy, they perform better, and they are able to find and keep good employment. This leads to millions of dollars in taxes paid, more houses purchased, more cars purchased, more investments in the stock market, children doing better in school, less policing in the community, less stress on the justice system, and the list goes on and on. My point is that we can take that $1.4 Billion and help pull people out of their emotional hole, which will heavily stimulate the economy, but it won't stimulate the prison systems.

Incarceration can also negatively impact future employment. Secure confinement contributes to barriers to education and employment that limit a person's ability to positively contribute to society, which may negatively impact public safety in the long term.

> *Because of the large number of overcrowded facilities, which often breed an environment of violence and chaos for young people, far from receiving effective treatment, young people with behavioral health problems may get worse in detention, not better.*[09]

> *Given the disproportionate use of juvenile detention facilities for youth of color one explanation [for the high incidence of youth with mental health disorders in facilities] may be that the juvenile justice system has become a de facto mental health system for poor and minority youth who are unable to access care through the formal mental health system.*[10]

> *Most juvenile justice systems do not have the facilities to properly screen or treat a young person with a mental health disorder, and if these young people are incarcerated the risks of victimization, self-injury, and suicide are high.*[11]

One academic study found that for one-third of incarcerated youth diagnosed with depression, the onset of the depression occurred after they began their incarceration.[12]

An article published in the medical journal, Pediatrics, concluded that, "The transition into incarceration itself may be responsible for some of the observed [increased mental illness in detention] effect."[13]

"When youth do not receive the mental health treatment that they need within facilities, their conditions only worsen."[14]

So, what is my point:

1. **Parents/Mentors**: Teach your children how to address police officers in a non-threatening way. Teach them to follow the directions of the officer to immediately de-escalate the situation. Teach them to keep their cool and to not get an attitude with officers or to "perform" in front of their friends or girlfriend/boyfriend. Consider role playing scenarios at home, especially if you drive a fancy car and the kids want to take it for a spin. We already know that young people in fancy cars have a very high possibility of being pulled over. I prepared my son this way when he was seventeen-years-old and borrowed my brand-new car to go to the movies. He was pulled over that night; he was agitated, but he kept his cool. I don't want to even imagine what could have happened if he would have lost his cool and said something inappropriate to the officer.

   If there is a problem and the officer is inappropriate in how your child is handled, tell your children not to argue with the police officer. Simply take down their badge number and call you to handle the situation further.

   Black, brown, and poor Americans will be stopped and harassed more often until the criminal justice *system* is changed. Arguing and resisting an officer will not change that system. The system has to be changed through our elected officials, through "peaceful" protests (as usually demonstrated by the Black Lives Matter movement) and "honest" dialog with lawmakers, the community, the judges, the police officers, etc.

2. **Police Officers**: I watched a Tulsa, OK police shooting video recently of an African-American man, Mr. Terence Crutcher, who had his hands raised as he walked toward his SUV that had broken down in the middle of the road. The officer in the helicopter above said, "That looks like a bad dude too, he must be on something." How would a person in a helicopter know that the man was bad or on something? I will let you

ponder that one. The man is then shot and killed by a female officer as he looked through the window of his truck. By the way, he was also tased by the other officer at the same time he was shot.

Why do you think the female officer felt the need to kill a man with his hand raised while looking through his car window? I understand that he was not complying with the requests of the officers to stop walking, but his hands were still raised, and he should not have lost his life. After talking to some local police officers, I was informed that officers are charged with controlling the situation as quickly as possible before it causes harm to the public or themselves. I just ask that you consider changing your weapons protocol to use tasers more often or aim at the legs instead of "one to the head, one to the chest," because that is not working out too well for the police department, the family of the victims, or the community. What if training was modified so that when there are two officers on the scene, one officer is locked and loaded, while the other officer has his/her taser pointed at the suspect? Additionally, the two must communicate as to who will shoot first, especially when the suspect is unarmed.

Many of the courthouses around the country have created a Veterans Treatment Court with a Veteran Mentor. This mentor will speak on behalf of the veteran and explain how the effects of being in a war zone has affected the mental health of the vet and played a pivotal part in the bad behavior that led to their court appearance. Some of our youth in the inner-city and the suburbs are suffering from childhood trauma and are living in their own mental war zone created in their homes, many times with the same symptoms as a person with PTSD. The child may have been sexually abused, lived in a homeless shelter, witnessed someone's death, or is in an extremely abusive family. That child is now in a serious emotional hole, and an arrest and subsequent visit to Juvenile Detention or prison will only send them deeper in that hole. This is where the system needs to be redesigned so that we ALL become part of the SOLUTION, instead of the current design which shows that it is part of societies overall PROBLEM. Let's make an effort to pull everyone OUT of the hole.

I know a young man who broke into someone's home at seventeen and was put on probation. He violated his probation by smoking marijuana. He went to prison for 36 months because of the probation violation. He was released early (18 months) at his family's request when they stood behind him in court (dressed professionally). He violated his probation again when he was out in the yard barefoot getting a cell phone charger out of his car (a policeman was patrolling at 3:00 am and asked for his ID). He was arrested the next day at the request of his parole officer. He spent another 45 days in jail and before releasing him, the judge threatened him with 30-years prison time if he saw him in his court again. This young man was again arrested 30 days later at the request of his parole officer for failure to provide a urine sample due to a misunderstanding of the instructions given by the parole officer. This young man was eventually given another 8 months in prison but will no longer be on probation once his sentence is complete, which means he won't have a curfew and he won't be tested for marijuana each week. This young man has a six-year old daughter and is in an emotional hole. Additionally, he is creating a hole for his daughter due to his long absences. Here is a classic case of a young man making bad decisions (by hurting himself through marijuana usage) that can send him to jail longer than a young wealthy white college student, Brock Turner of Stanford University, who was convicted of raping a young female student while she was unconscious behind a garbage can on campus. He served 6 months in jail.

It is time for the community to come together with churches, counseling organizations, police officers, etc. and develop a plan that will help our young people to climb out of the hole, not push them deeper into it.

QUESTIONS:

1. Do teenagers in your community have negative perceptions of the local police?

   _____

   _____

2. Do you have an idea of how police officers can work closely with the youth in your community?

   _____

   _____

3. What can you do to make the relations between police and local youth better?

   _____

   _____

"If you don't build your dream someone will hire you to help build theirs."

- Tony Gaskins

SUCCESS TOOLS
FOR
YOUR FUTURE

"In order to get burnt out, you must have already been on fire."

- Tim Wise

TOOL #1

HOW TO START A CONVERSATION WITH AN ABSENT FATHER

Most children would like to have a weekly conversation with their biological father, whether he is in jail, lives across town, in another state/country, or whether everyone lives under the same roof. If the conversations are months apart, this will cause the child to deal with certain conscious or subconscious emotional feelings of abandonment, causing them to act out and/or shut out. Some fathers may reach out to their children, but because they are met with some sort of resistance, they may feel as though the child is not interested in a stronger relationship. It takes two people to keep the relationship going. The phone works on both sides. Many times, the father says, "If my kids want to talk, they have my number and they can pick up the phone and call." At times the child or adult child says, "My father was not there for me, so if he wants a relationship, he knows my number and he can pick up the phone and call." Can you say, "STANDSTILL"! Each side is waiting on the other side to create the relationship. The child says, "Well, he has a relationship with my brother and his family." And the father says, "Well, my son and his family CALLS ME all of the time and we have a great relationship." Bottom line: The phone works both ways. You both have a responsibility to keep the relationship strong. We don't have forever to get the relationship right, so stop being stubborn and create the relationship... NOW! Tomorrow is not promised.

Most common questions asked by you when the phone rings and it is your long-lost father:

1. Where have you been?

2. Did you ever think about me?

3. Why haven't I seen you in ten years?

4. Why are you calling me now?

5. Do you understand that our family needed you to help us when we were struggling?

6. Do you know that I am a good person? Do you care?

There are many reasons why a father may have been absent from his children. Here are the most common reasons (although none are viable excuses):

151

1. Drug or alcohol abuse (dealing with their own trauma that put them in an emotional hole)

2. Your father was exhausted and gave up after your mother verbally or physically abused him and refused to allow him to see you.

3. He was not sure how to find you.

4. Your mother may have never told him she was pregnant (she feared your father would take you away from her).

5. He was in prison for many years.

6. Was transferred due to military orders and lost contact.

7. He may have been overwhelmed because multiple women were pregnant at the same time.

8. When things go tough, his grandfather left his family, his father left his family, so he left his family (generational curse).

9. He was threatened with bodily harm by your mother's parents, siblings, or uncles, so he fled.

10. Your father and your mother never were on the same page with anything, and she said she never wanted to see him again.

He was probably an emotionally unbalanced teenager who grew up to be an emotionally unbalanced adult who fell into his own emotional hole due to the death, absence, or non-support of a biological parent, or maybe even the death of a child, sibling, or friend.

I am just trying to shed a positive light on the situation. None of them are valid reasons for your father's absence from you.

Dad, Let's Talk...

When you talk to your father for the first time in years, try very hard not to get angry and allow your emotions to take over the call. Listen to what he has to say. Some fathers reach out because they have regret, they may have a terminal illness, and others reach out because they miss their children, understanding that they made a lot of mistakes in the past. Many fathers are scared to reach out after you are 18-years-old because they fear the rejection and don't know what to say to you at that point. Some fathers may have been afraid to come around for years because they were threatened by your mother's family because of a domestic dispute that took place early in the relationship.

It is very important to allow your father back into your life (if it is not detrimental to your life due to illegal activity). If there is illegal activity in your father's life, then a phone relationship may be a better choice. You are allowing him back in your life for your own sake, not necessarily for his sake. We need our parents more than we realize, no matter how many times we say we don't. Having relationships with our biological parents throughout our entire lives just makes for a life that has less stress in it, provides us with mentoring, counseling, and understanding from someone who is made up of the same DNA we are. The generational information that can be gleaned from your biological father may be the information you need to understand your personality, character, drive, and talents. It helps for more fulfilling relationships with your own children, spouse, best friends, and supervisors (emotionally balanced work life). From 5 to 75-years-old, everyone wants to know that the two people who were responsible for their birth loves them and are proud of them. It is an innate need that is very hard for us to control, so allow him access to your life for YOUR own benefit.

One of my clients reached out to his father after one of our group sessions. This young man is twenty-three years-old and hadn't seen or spoken to his father in over seventeen years. Here's what he had to say, "Mr. Cunningham, after our first session last week, I immediately reached out to my father on social media. I sent him a message in his inbox. He replied to my message saying that he was sorry, and he wanted to talk. So, we did. I cried like a baby when we got off of the phone. I didn't even know those emotions were there. Later he sent me another message stating that he wants to start a relationship, but I did not respond to it. I don't know what to talk about, it's been a long time." I encouraged him to start a *weekly* conversation with his father.

Here are some things to converse about if you struggle to find a subject:

1. **Sports**: Most fathers have a favorite sports team. Check out the team's website for news prior to calling your father so that you are aware of current events with his team.

2. **Family and Legacy**: Talk about his parents, siblings, and/or get updates on your step-sisters and brothers. You can also learn about your family tree (i.e. grandparents, great grandparents, etc.). What were the different professions on his

side of the family? It could explain why you like music, math, science, or engineering.

3. **Hometown**: Talk about your hometown and/or your father's hometown. Are there any famous people from your hometown? What was your father's upbringing like?

4. **College**: Talk about the college you want to attend and how he can help you make your dream a reality. Ask him to go with you on a college visit. Get him involved in your life and allow him to help you make some future choices in your life.

5. **Hobbies**: Talk about cars, boats, fishing, bowling, painting, music, etc.

6. **Favorite TV Shows**: Ask him about his favorite shows.

7. **Advice**: You will be surprised at how similar you are to your parents, even when they didn't raise you. Seek their advice on certain things that happen in your life. We actually need our parents more after eighteen-years-old than we did as a child, because life will continually throw challenges at us that we will need our parents to help us navigate (See Four Personal Pillars of Trust)

8. **Music**: If you like a particular style of music, ask your father to rank the top 10 performers of all time.

Also, if you don't have a good memory, you may want to have a notepad nearby in order to capture some of your conversations, especially concerning the history of the family, and to be sure that you ask him everything that may be on your mind. But, don't try to learn everything in one conversation. Give the information time to process and slowly rebuild the trust. You will be glad that you did.

"If you don't design your own life plan, chances are you'll fall into someone else's plan. And guess what they have planned for you? Not much."

– Jim Rohn

TOOL #2
How to Move Past Broken Promises

Below are some broken promises that cause children to rebel against their parents:

1. I will come and pick you up this weekend and take you to the park.

2. I will call you back tomorrow.

3. I will send you some school clothes next week.

4. I will send you some money and a gift for your birthday.

5. I will be in town next week and I will come by and see you.

When promises are broken, it will affect the child/children in a negative way. Unfortunately, if someone tries to step-in and do those things in place of your parent, it doesn't stop the feeling of being rejected by the person who you are yearning to give you unconditional love. Some parents make promises because they want to be liked, and they want to have something nice to say to you to make you smile while having a conversation. When they make the promises, many times, they believe that they are going to put action behind their words, but they don't. They either let the stress of life and finances stop them from going into action or they get resistance from the current spouse or significant other. Your parent may not have the nerve to call you to cancel the plans or they fear disappointing you again.

Eric Thomas stated, "People with good intentions make promises, people with good character keep them."

How to Get Past Broken Promises:

When a person shows you who they are, through their actions, it is unlikely that you will see them do something different unless they have had a major shift in their life (forgiveness, counseling, finding their life's purpose, and/or developing a solid spiritual foundation by giving their life to God and studying their Bible). Here's how to handle it when a parent makes a promise:

1. Don't believe the promises, as this is a way for you to control what happens to you and not let others control your thoughts or feelings. If they keep the promise, great. If not, you will not be disappointed. Don't get an attitude and say, "I will believe it when I see it." Always stay in control and keep a kind demeanor.

2. Forgive your parent for all the times that they have disappointed you. You must remain in control of your thoughts.

3. Understand that your parents are not perfect. They probably had an absent mother/father or experienced a tragic event in their own lives.

Expectation Management

It is great to know what everyone in your life expects from you (parents, significant others, siblings, children, supervisors, etc.) Simply ask, "Mom or dad, what do you expect from me as your son or daughter?" Wait for an answer. If they reply, "nothing," then state "Then I would assume that I could never do anything to disappoint you." This should get a reply.

When they finish talking, then ask "Is it okay if I tell you what I expect from you as my mom/dad"? Then respond by saying, "I expect for you to love me unconditionally. I expect for you to tell me when I am headed in the wrong direction in life. I expect for you to help me get into college. I expect for you to do what you say or tell me if plans change. I expect for you to talk to me without yelling if possible. I expect for you to believe in me and tell me that you are proud of me. I expect for us to have a loving conversation at least once a week. I expect for you to let me know if you are somehow disappointed in me, etc.

If you want to see change in any of your loved ones, then it will happen through the 5 Ways of Conquering Your Life. Forgiveness/spirituality is always the best start, and it won't cost you a thing to forgive people and to start your spiritual walk.

TOOL #3

HOW TO WRITE LETTERS OF FORGIVENESS

The letters must have 3 components:

1. Include all of your negative emotions in the letter (this will be the last time these emotions are expressed).

2. Include what you have learned from this situation that is positive (even if the only thing that you learned was that you survived, and that the ordeal made you a stronger person).

   a. Did this event make you a kinder, more empathetic person to your friends and family?
   b. Did this event make you a better parent?
   c. Did this event make you a hard worker?
   d. Did this event make you want to become more successful?
   e. Did this event make you seek out your life's passion where you are always lending a helping hand to other people?
   f. Did this event bring you closer to God or caused you to study his principles?
   g. Did this event cause you to want to do more with your life?

3. End each letter with "I love myself, I forgive myself, and I forgive you".

4. After reading each letter 3 times, BURN IT (RIP IT UP and FLUSH IT if under 18-years-old).

NOTE: If you can't burn it right away, based on your age or residence (college dorms, military dorms, detention centers, etc.), then *RIP IT UP* into tiny little pieces and flush it down the toilet. It is important to watch it as it disappears in the toilet. The best place to burn the letters are in the kitchen sink (on the side where the garbage disposal is located).

Balling the letter up and throwing it away will not produce the desired effect.

This process takes 30 minutes. It is a proven process for hundreds of people who have actually tried it. It has a 99% success rate in relieving stress and helping you focus on your future.

Although this method may appear silly in your mind, I would ask, "how is your way working?" Take this 30-minute challenge. You will be glad you did. Be sure to send us an email or a video and tell us how it has helped you. Email us at info@rodcunninghamspeaks.com.

Sample Letter to a *Non-Supportive Parent*

Diagram T-1

Dec 1, 2018

Dear Mom or Dad,

I am writing this letter to let you know that I am ***disappointed and hurt*** by the fact that you never accepted me for who I am and only for who you wanted me to be. I am an artist, I am different, and I am OK with who I am and who I have become. I have always felt that I was last on your list of priorities. I can count on one hand how many times you have told me that you love me and that you are proud of me. It is very important for me to know that I matter to you.

Starting today, I have decided that I am not going to allow you or anyone else to disappoint me again and from this day forward, I will take control of my mind and my life with the help of God. I have the right to choose any emotion that I want at this time in my life, and I CHOOSE LOVE.

Through this experience, **I have learned** that I am a very strong person who loves to help others. My siblings and I are closer, and I am also very close to my grandmother because of this entire situation, so it has served my life in a great way.

I would like you to know that I LOVE MYSELF, I FORGIVE MYSELF, and I FORGIVE YOU.

Sincerely,

John

----------------*BURN THE LETTER* AFTER READING IT 3 TIMES----------------------

OR

----------------*RIP IT and FLUSH IT* if under 18-Years-Old ----------------------

Sample Letter to a *Deceased Parent*

Diagram T-2

Dec 1, 2018

Dear Mom or Dad,

     I am writing this letter to let you know that I miss you dearly. Although you have been gone from me for 3 years now, I want you to know that you would be so proud of my accomplishments. I graduated from high school and I just completed my technical training as a certified nursing assistant.

     I remember all the things you taught me, and I am also helping young children in elementary school by being a tutor and mentor. I also volunteer to feed the homeless once per month. I started dating recently and we have been talking about marriage. I truly miss you and you will always remain in my heart. I will be sure to tell my future children and grandchildren all about you.

     I have not been as active and vibrant as I used to be, but I have decided that I will take control of my mind and my life with the help of God. I was told that I can start to change and control my mind at any time and make a U-turn in life. Also, if I continue to grieve, I will seek counselling so that I can talk to someone who can help me sort through my emotions and guide me to a better future.

     I know that I have become a better, stronger person and I have learned that I can do anything I put my mind to.

     I would like you to know that I LOVE MYSELF, I FORGIVE MYSELF and I FORGIVE YOU for leaving me here to figure out life without you helping and guiding me.

Sincerely,

Jake

----------------**BURN THE LETTER** AFTER READING IT 3 TIMES----------------------

OR

----------------**RIP IT and FLUSH IT** if under 18-Years-Old ----------------------

Sample Letter to *People Who Have Hurt You*

Diagram T-3

Dec 1, 2018

Dear Mom, Dad, Uncle, Cousin, Mr. Bob, etc.,

I am writing this letter to let you know that I am ***angry, hurt, and disappointed*** by your actions. You said and did some things to me that has caused me emotional pain for the past 7 years.

Starting today, I have decided that I am not going to allow you or anyone else to hurt me again, and from this day forward, I will take control of my mind and my life with the help of God. I have the right to choose any emotion that I want at this time in my life, and I CHOOSE LOVE.

I have learned so much about myself from this ordeal. I am a kinder, gentler person who cares about the plight of others in the community. My compassion for helping young children is very strong.

I would like you to know that I LOVE MYSELF, I FORGIVE MYSELF, and I FORGIVE YOU.

Sincerely,

Tammy

-----------------***BURN THE LETTER* AFTER READING IT 3 TIMES**---------------------

OR

-----------------***RIP IT and FLUSH IT* if under 18-Years-Old** ---------------------

Sample Letter to a *Friend Who Committed Suicide*

Diagram T-4

Dec 1, 2018

Dear David,

I am writing this letter to let you know that I am miss you dearly. Although you have been gone from me for two years now, I want you to know that I still blame myself for not acting on the signs you displayed while you were in emotional pain. We have shared some great secrets and I will still keep them to myself forever. I graduated from high school last week and I plan to attend Florida State University in August.

I remember all of the fun things we did together, and I plan to name my first child after you. If it is a girl, her name will be Davida... LOL. I finally got up the nerve to ask Amelia out on a date and we have been dating for 6 months now. I truly miss you and you will always remain in my heart. I will be sure to tell my future children and grandchildren all about you.

I have not been as active and vibrant as I used to be, but I have decided that I will take control of my mind and my life with the help of God. I was told that I can start to change my mind at any time and make a U-turn in life. Also, if I continue to grieve, I will seek counselling so that I can talk to someone who can help me sort through my emotions and guide me to a better future.

I have LEARNED so much about teenage suicide since you left, and I have decided to become a therapist for teens who experienced childhood trauma. I am also a better person because I understand that tomorrow is not promised, so I will live my greatest life today.

I would like you to know that I no longer blame myself for your choices, I LOVE MYSELF, I FORGIVE MYSELF and I FORGIVE YOU for leaving me here to figure out life without you helping and guiding me.

Sincerely,

John-John

-----------------*BURN THE LETTER* **AFTER READING IT 3 TIMES**---------------------

OR

-----------------*RIP IT and FLUSH IT* **if under 18-Years-Old** ---------------------

"Every child wants to know two things from their parents. Do you love me unconditionally and are you proud of me?"

\- Roderick Cunningham

TOOL # 4
WHO TO CALL FOR HELP

The referral information below is for use by parents, teachers, mentors, and children. Teenagers, please use the information to help your friends and family members in need. Our friends will reach out to us in time of crisis and usually we don't know what to tell them to do. Now we know where to send them.

Nationwide 24-Hour Hotline

Alcohol and Drug Abuse

National Drug Information Treatment and Referral Hotline……………1-800-662-HELP (4357)
Drug Hotline……………………………………………………………1-800-333-4313

Local:	
Local:	

Family and Individual Crisis Hotline

Boys Town Suicide and Crisis Line (Adults and Children) ………………… 1-800-448-3000
National Youth Crisis Hotline…………………………………………1-800-442-HOPE (4673)
Suicide Hotline………………………………………………………1-800-333-4313
Covenant House Hotline…………………………………………1-800-999-9999

Local:	
Local:	

Sexual Assault / Rape, Child Abuse, and Domestic Violence

RAINN National Rape Crisis Hotline……………………………………… 1-800-656-HOPE (4673)
National Child Abuse Hotline……………………………………… 1-800-25-ABUSE (22873)
Childhelp USA…………………………………………………………… 1-800-422-4453
National Domestic Violence Hotline…………………………………… 1-800-799-SAFE (7233)

Local:	
Local:	

Crisis Counseling and Services for Runaways

National Runaway Switchboard………………………………………… 1-800-621-4000

Local:	

"Don't go around saying the world owes you a living. The world owes you nothing. It was here first."

\- Mark Twain

TOOL # 5
RELATED MOVIES AND DOCUMENTARIES

Many times, we watch movies for entertainment and totally miss the message. As we mature in life and start to experience life on a new level, and a movie we saw ten years ago, suddenly has new meaning. This simply means that certain life experiences and our education will allow certain antennas in our brain to get aroused, looking for solutions to our situation or the situation of a loved one. For my mentors and course facilitators, I challenge you to review the movies prior to using them in the classroom and be ready to discuss. Remember, the movie will mean something different to each person based on their experiences. The movie can be used as homework or it can be watched during your week long or summer long sessions. For parents, I recommend watching the Rated R movies as education to help you understand your children and what it feels like to be in a deep emotional hole. These movies represent deep emotional holes that may or may not have been diagnosed by a professional therapist (psychiatrist).

Inside Out (2015) Directed by Pete Docter/Ronne Del Carmen [PG].. .... Youth Mental Health

Antwone Fisher (2002) Directed by Denzel Washington [PG-13]............... Foster Care/ Childhood Sexual Trauma

Acrimony (2018) Directed by Tyler Perry.. Depression/ Borderline Personality Disorder

Perks of Being a Wallflower (2012) Directed by Stephen Chbosky [PG-13]..Youth Mental Health

Beautiful Mind (2001) Directed by Ron Howard [PG-13]............................. Schizophrenia

Love and Mercy (2014) Directed by Bill Pohlad [PG-13] .... Bipolar Disorder

The Soloist (2009) Directed by Joe Wright [PG-13]...................................... Schizophrenia

As Good as it Gets (1997) Directed by James L. Brooks [PG-13]............. Obsessive-Compulsive (OCD)

Rain Man (1988) Directed by Barry Levinson [R]... Autism and Empathy

Mr. Jones (1993) Directed by Mike Figgis [R].. Bipolar Disorder

Primal Fear (1996) Directed by Gregory Hoblit [R].. Bipolar disorder

Infinitely Polar Bear (2014) Directed by Maya Forbes [R]............................. Bipolar Disorder

Silver Linings Playbook (2012) Directed by David O. Russell [R]................... Bipolar Disorder

Ray (2004) Directed by Taylor Hackford [R]... Childhood Trauma

The Skeleton Twins (2014) Directed by Craig Johnson [R]............................ Depression

Good Will Hunting (1993) Directed by Gus Van Sant [R]............................... Depression

REFERENCES

[01] Centers for Disease Control and Prevention, 2017, Antidepressant Use Among Persons Aged 12 and Over: United States, 2011–2014, https://www.cdc.gov/nchs/products/databriefs/db283.htm

[02] The Bible. New International Version, New King James Version, and The Message Bible, http://www.Bible.com: 1 Corinthians 13:4-7

[03] Naim, Rania, (2016). Thought Catalog, http://thoughtcatalog.com/rania-naim/2016/02/the-7-kinds-of-love-and-how-they-can-help-you-define-yours-according-to-the-ancient-greeks/

[04] American Counseling Association, 2018, What is Professional Counseling? **https://www.counseling.org/aca-community/learn-about-counseling/what-is-counseling**

[05] Neurolinguistic Programming, Tad James Company, 2016, http://www.nlpcoaching.com/

[06] Growing Up with a Single Parent, Sara McLanahan, 1994, Harvard University Press

[07] Transforming Conflict, National Centre for Restorative Approaches in Youth Settings, 2016, http://www.transformingconflict.org/content/restorative-approaches-0

[09] Coalition for Juvenile Justice, Handle with Care: Meeting the Mental Health Needs of Young Offenders, CJJ 2000 Annual Report to the President, Congress and OJJDP (Washington, D.C.: CJJ, 2001)

[10] Chief Probation Officers of California and California Mental Health Directors Association, 2008, Page iii.

[11] National Mental Health Association, Mental health treatment for youth in the juvenile justice system: A compendium of promising practices. (Alexandria, VA: National Mental Health Association, 2004)

[12] J.H. Kashani, G.W. Manning, D.H. McKnew, L. Cytryn, J.F. Simonds, and P.C. Wooderson, "Depression Among Incarcerated Delinquents," Psychiatry Resources 3 (1980): 185-191.

[13] C.B. Forrest, E. Tambor, A.W. Riley, M.E. Ensminger, and B. Starfield, "The Health Profile of Incarcerated Male Youths," Pediatrics 105, no. 1 (2000): 286-291.

[14] Cost of Confinement. (2009, May). Retrieved from Justice Policy Institute: http://www.justicepolicy.org/images/upload/09_05_rep_costsofconfinement_jj_ps.pdf

CONTACT US

Training Courses for Students (Age 10 to 30-yrs old)

One-on-One Coaching with Rod Cunningham

Train-the-Trainer Certification Courses

★ Mentors

★ City Youth Directors

★ Non-Profit Staff Dealing with Youth

★ Adoption Agencies

★ Social Workers

★ School Detention Teachers

★ Veterans Affairs/PTSD Hotline Employees

Speaking Engagements

★ Colleges

★ Police Departments

★ Youth Groups

★ Prisons/Juvenile Detention Centers

★ Schools

★ Parents

★ Teachers/Counselors

★ Veterans Affairs/PTSD Hotline Employees

Info@rodcunninghamspeaks.com

www.rodcunninghamspeaks.com

ACKNOWLEDGEMENTS

I feel a deep sense of gratitude to my family, friends, and clients for their assistance in completing this book. To my wife, Valerie, as in all things, you have been extremely supportive and understanding as I worked to complete this project. Thank you for your patience and unconditional love. You've always had my front and my back.

To my three adult children, I appreciate you and the love that we share and continue to share as a family. Amber (Thomas Davis, SSG, U.S. Army), thank you for your constant love and communication. I love the fact that we talk every day, no matter where you are in the world. Dexter (Gianletty), our deep conversations on life and love has helped me narrow the focus of my book as well as my coaching business. You are intelligent beyond your years. Erika, thank you for being a great example of love and patience and for illustrating this workbook.

To the loving memory of my awesome Mother, Jacqui Granger of Jacksonville, FL (Sep 1952 – Dec 2014). You left us too soon. You wanted me to add these words in my book, "From Sea to Shining Sea," so here it is. I love you and miss you very much. You taught me what unconditional love is all about. All that I am, I am because of your love, patience, and guidance. I humbly dedicate this book to you and your legacy.

To the happy memory of my wonderful Mother-In-Law, Cheryl Townsend of Tampa, FL, by way of Ft. Wayne, IN (Jan 1950 – May 2015). Thank you for your years of mentorship, love, and acceptance as a son. It was a joy being with you in your final days and learning from your life experiences. Thank you for encouraging me to write this book and thanks for being an awesome Mom to me for over 20 years.

To my cousin, who is like a brother, Bishop Roderick S. Love thank you for your spiritual guidance and holding my feet to the fire.

To my best friends, Edgar Lagressa Mathis, II and Derrell Bonnett, of Jax, FL, thank you for your encouragement and 35 years of friendship.

To the District Fire Chief of Jacksonville, Terrance Jones, thanks for all the wisdom you have shared with me. I enjoy our long philosophical talks.

To my all of my aunts, uncles, and cousins in Jax, FL, thanks for looking after of my mom while I served my country and for constantly keeping me safe through your prayers.

To my fraternity brothers, of Omega Psi Phi Fraternity, Inc., thanks for your continued support and friendship during the great times and not so great times of my life.
- Bro D. Simon (US Army Lt Colonel retired) of Tampa, a great friend and mentor
- Bro Dionni Henderson (USAF Master Sergeant) of Biloxi, MS, a true friend and inspiration
- Bro Antoine Jenkins (US Marine Corps Lt Colonel retired), awesome mentor
- Bro Derrick Crowley (USAF Chief Master Sergeant ret.), awesome career mentor
- Bro Michael Mays (USAF Master Sergeant ret.), great mentor and counselor

Other fraternity brothers that I can always count on when called: Brothers Richard Swoope (USA Colonel ret.), Rodney Lewis (USMC Lt Colonel retired), Michael Harris (USA Lt Colonel ret.), , Kevin Holmes (USAF Master Sergeant ret.), Darrell "Boe" Harris (USA Sergeant First Class ret.), Bert "BJ" Gore, Jr. (USAF MSgt ret.), and Julius Davis (CEO, VoltAir Engineering). A special thanks to my home chapter in Tampa, Epsilon Mu Mu, my chapter while in Gulfport, MS., Iota Upsilon, and my adopted chapter in St. Petersburg, Eta Rho. Also, special thanks go out to Bro Rev. Watson L. Haynes, CEO of Pinellas County Urban League for your continued support and excellent mentorship. Friendship is Essential to the Soul.

To my Air Force family. Thank you for the great team support for 29 years and encouraging me to take my message to teenagers to help them find their emotional intelligence early in life. Thanks to my former leaders; Major General Mark Anthony Brown and wife Vivian for your excellent leadership and support to Valerie and me, General Patrick C. Higby for your friendship and your strong belief in me, and Colonel Beena Maharaj for believing in me and my ability to develop the future leaders of the Air Force. Thanks to my USAF mentors; CMSgt (ret) Cameron Kirksey, CMSgt (ret) Patricia Thornton, and SMSgt (ret) and City of Tampa Fire Chief Tom Forward, your leadership and mentorship is unmatched. Thanks to my cousin, Lt Col Phelemon Williams, for your love and continued support.

To my teenage and young adult family at the Pinellas County Job Corp. The information you shared with me in our sessions will help thousands of young people to overcome their childhood trauma and emotional hurts.

ABOUT THE AUTHOR

 Rod Cunningham was born to a 15-year-old mother in the housing projects of Jacksonville, Florida. His father was 19-years-old when he died two weeks before his birth. Rod watched his step-father verbally and physically abuse his mother for 7 years, leading to he and his mother escaping the home in the middle of the night. They eventually divorced, leaving him to grow up without any adult male influence, which led to him having a daughter at 19-years-old, in search of his manhood. The choice to join the Air Force was the best decision of his life, getting plenty of male influence from men of honor, dignity, and character.

Rod retired from the U.S. Air Force after 29 years of dedicated service to our country in February 2016 as a Chief Master Sergeant (E-9). He developed leadership programs for the Air Force. In his role as Dean of Students, Air Force Technical Training School in Biloxi, MS, he personally counseled, mentored, and coached 2,500 students annually and developed a student mentorship program that decreased academic attrition rate by 90% in three years. After retirement, he joined the Pinellas County Urban League as Vice President of Corporate Relations where he successfully developed and managed a weekly poverty reduction program for 23 families in low-income communities.

He is currently a transformational speaker, youth empowerment coach, and community leader. He has participated in over 50 leadership and community panels, has delivered over 300 speeches and he is humbled by the fact that he has individually counseled, mentored, and empowered over 9,000 teenagers and young adults between the ages of 10 and 30 over the last six years who entrusted him with their innermost secrets. He mentors juvenile detainees, works with the Urban League's Youth and Empowerment Programs, developed and taught a manhood course for the Pinellas County Job Corps called "Confront and Conquer, The Journey to Manhood", and mentors 40+ young men and women each week.

Rod is regarded by many community leaders and young adults around the country as a leader who is passionate about the success of others. Rod speaks about facing your past to own your future. He has a simple, yet impactful way of showing how the events of life can put many of us in an emotional hole of varying degrees. Rod has the ability to, "get in the hole", because he's been there. He teaches you how to quickly CLIMB out before life's next major negative event. His techniques are designed to change a child, a family, a school, a community, a city, and a nation. Whether it is a one-on-one session, a 15-minute speech, a 1-hour speech, or a week-long seminar, Rod can help change the direction of your life!

Rod and his wife Valerie reside in the beautiful, St. Petersburg, Florida. He has three adult children and five grandchildren.

Made in the USA
Columbia, SC
19 July 2019